Thon Stanley Berne &
In appreciation of their admiration of
this book.
My thanks.
Eivind Dahlberg
Mar. 21. 58
(Terreno) Palma de Mallorca.
Espana.

The Sorrows of Priapus

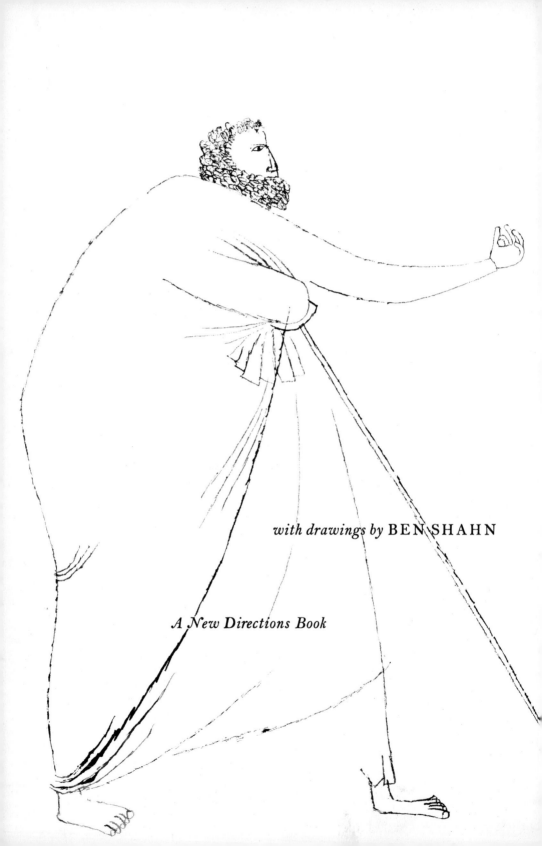

with drawings by BEN SHAHN

A New Directions Book

EDWARD DAHLBERG

The Sorrows of **P**riapus

Copyright © 1957 by NEW DIRECTIONS
Library of Congress catalog card number 57-6942
Printed in the United States of America by the
Crafton Graphic Company.

typography and layout / Elaine Lustig

NEW DIRECTIONS BOOKS are published by James Laughlin
at Norfolk, Connecticut
New York Office: 333 Sixth Avenue (14)

for SIR HERBERT READ:

Dear Herbert: The poor bring a pair of turtle doves to the altar, or grains of maize to Quetzalcoatl; and I have no better alms than this book to dedicate to the genius of your heart which is the limbeck where you brew the honey of your poesy and prose. This is pauper's thanks for friendship and kindness; let it not be said that I hoard my love or gratitude without which the earth wanders away from our heads, feet and arms. Each poem or book is Demeter's quest for Persephone, who is the furrow, seed-time, and affection, or an act against Nature.

AUTHOR'S NOTE

This is a fable and not natural history. The polestar of the writer is a legendary book, using geography, the beasts in the earth and in the sea, and voyages, as the source of maxims, mirth and an American myth. To accomplish this many narratives have been employed; in two instances I have done little more than paraphrase Athenaeus and Aristotle's *Animals* which I also regard as a remarkable fable though both Buffon and Humboldt held the Stagirite in the highest esteem. Plato, St. Augustine, Clemens of Alexandria, Pausanias, Hakluyt, Diego de Landa, Sahagun, Pigafetta, and innumerable other mythographers and discoverers have been my inward seas, tides and life. This is a book for brave readers and poets.

Edward Dahlberg

DRAWINGS

greek with crutch *frontispiece*
triciput 1
nude with drapery on shoulder 5
owl 9
turtle 12
grasshopper 13
old goat 17
monkey 21
profile 24
pomegranate 28
flowers 31
sirens 33
swan 37
fat drunkard asleep 41
nude on partridge 44
bee 45
three-breasted woman 49
adam and eve 53
medusa 57
two primitive figures 59
drowning man 61
man with arrow 65
man as stars 68
two primitive figures with spears 71
struggle between animal and masked man 75
two eagles 78
frog among flowers 79
pomegranate plant 83
grazing horse 87
four-armed figure on bull 91
unknown animal 94
stag 95
eagle 98
woman with snakes 101
winged boar 105
cock 109
zoanthus 111
erinys 113
young bull 115
galley with buildings 116
primitive horses 119

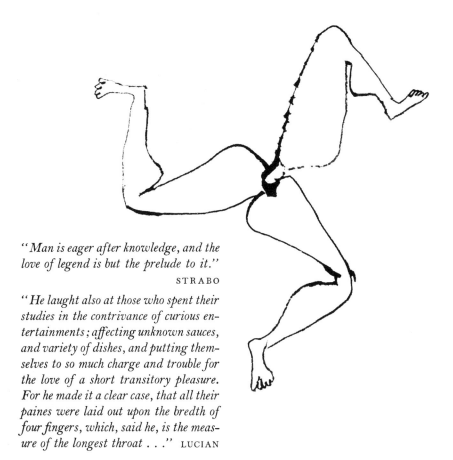

> "*Man is eager after knowledge, and the love of legend is but the prelude to it.*"
>
> STRABO

> "*He laught also at those who spent their studies in the contrivance of curious entertainments; affecting unknown sauces, and variety of dishes, and putting themselves to so much charge and trouble for the love of a short transitory pleasure. For he made it a clear case, that all their paines were laid out upon the bredth of four fingers, which, said he, is the measure of the longest throat . . .*" LUCIAN

PROLOGUE

Sing Venus Hetaera; Priam had fifty wives, and Darius went to battle with three hundred and fifty concubines; sing Venus the Courtesan who has sunk the Theban towers. Aspasia sacked all Hellas, and Gnathaena pillaged the pockets of the poet Diphilus.

List the courtesans as Homer catalogues the ships at windy Ilium: Chrysis, Corone, Ischas, and Antycra, who quelled many Argives, and relieved Pericles, Aristotle, Aristippus and Sophocles; let them be recollected, and savored once more, and thrice again as an ox's chine.

There were Telesis, Dippthese, and her whoring mother, and Theolyte who grew rotten hands and hunkers at her trade; the dearest thighs of virgins came from Ithya and Hellade. At Abydos, one of the four great towns of fishy Hellespont, there was a temple of Venus the Prostitute. When Solon saw it was impossible to bridle the youths of Athens he imported tarts from Corinth and Megara, and employed some of the revenue which the women earned to erect a statue to Venus the Strumpet. Aspasia and her college for whores are as necessary to Athens as abstemious Socrates.

Pious Greeks bring cakes and sesamum and the orchites of stags and wolves to chaste Artemis the Huntress who rules Ephesus where every year they hold a Whore's Festival called Aphrodisia. Lacedaemon has given us Cottina whose name is a rumor of pleasure throughout the Levant, and she is immortal, for a brothel bore her dear name. Give homage to Phryne, for in her heyday, when she gathered capers, she was worth the thirty keels Nestor commanded at Troy.

At the rising of the Dogstar the swordfish go mad for the female; boars propagate their species with joy; vipers take a long time when they are intertwined. Consider the snows of the Alps; Eudoxus and Euclid winter all lechery; the intellect is a hot plague, loud with boasts. The cephali have large heads; cuttlefish have as much ink as Euripides; skin is slime and sand. Men at first, says Empedokles, were eels, graylings, polypi, seathrushes.

Avoid cucumbers, gourds, violets, watercress, and the soft blows and amatory kicks from the Marathonian women. Boiled torpedo done in oil and wine is indigestible and inflammatory; one bed and one wife is philosophy; age withers all wives; the sea-cuckoo has a dry rump which lames the tribe of fish; 'tis best. Copulation is a dangerous pastime.

Darius promised any man who invented a new pleasure a large reward. Cotys, King of Thrace, prepared a marriage feast for Artemis, and waited for hours for her to come to his bed. The sole testament and bequest of the physician Nicostratus was a huge quantity of hellebore which he left to his whore. The great Stagirite named his ethics after his son Nichomachus who was the issue of a harlot. Ptolemy Philadelphus lay with Didyma, Billisticha, Agathoclea, and Stratonica, for whom he built many monuments along the seashore. Clito, Alexander's cupbearer, wore only the lightest tunic, and held in her right hand a cornucopia, which is a sign of seminal wealth. Many splendid houses in the ancient world bore the names Myrtium, Mnesis, Pothina, although Mnesis was a flute player and Myrtium a notorious doxy. Agathoclea was Ptolemy Philopator's prostitute; she ruled him who was supposed to govern Egypt, and ruined both. Hieronymus, the tyrant, fell in love with a common bitch he met in a house of ill-fame, and he made her queen of Syracuse. The king of Pergamus was the offspring of a flute player. Ptolemy, one of the Hundred Companions, was the issue of a whore by Alexander's father Philip.

Greek worship was a theology of bawds. The statues of Demeter, the hymns to Persephatta, and the paintings of Daphne were a scholium on venery. Alcman invented the first songs of lust, and Nicander, the poet, called the goddess of amours Aphrodite Kalligluttus, the strumpet with the marvelous rump. Praxiteles thought the bitch of love resembled the figure of his mistress, Cratine, and all the painters, who paid visits to Phryne to copy those parts which send men to Tartarus or to the almshouse, were patrons of the *muliebria*.

The nereids, nymphs, hamadryads, naiads came out of the sporting houses of elysium. Aphrodite, the lover of virilia, sprang from the scum of the sea; others say from the gore from the genitals of Uranus. The masculine gods were whoremongers; Hephaestus, the humpback brazier, as licentious as a fuller, tailor, weaver, potter, was miserable until he married Aphrodite who forsook him for Mars. There was Zeus the Ant, so named because he assumed the shape of that insect in order to have intercourse with Eurymedusa. Jove could never empty his testicles; he lay with Europa, and threw the orchites of a ram upon the breasts of Demeter because he had raped her. Every watery image aroused Poseidon, who deflowered Amphitrite, Anymone, Alope, Alcyone, Hippothoe, Chione, who are sea foam, breakers, tidal waves. The titans were insatiable; Hercules gathered fifty maidenheads in one night. He had at least fifty offspring and was not regarded as exceptional in copulation.

The rituals of these gods and goddesses are mystical sexual bouts. Semiramis, another title for Astarte or Ashtoreth, slew every man after she had enjoyed him. The Athenian women celebrated the rape of Persephone, which they called the mysteries of Thesmophoria; the frenzied women at this ceremony carried the sacred chest of Bacchus which contained his prepuce. They baked sesame cakes, pyramidal cookies, and brought lumps of salt which were emblems of Priapus. In the orgies of Cybele the drums were beat, there was the sounding of cymbals, and the fig branches that were held aloft resembled the phalloi. The comb, marjoram, and lamp of Themis represented her secret parts.

Beauty is the tomb of the race of men who crave ruin. There was no wanton running after women when Numa and King Tullus Hostilius ruled, for justice and the character of woman were held in higher regard than her navel or licentious toes, though the Sabine maids were most appealing. "Beauty is...a short-lived tyranny," remarked Socrates. Theophrastus called it a silent deceit. Each person has a deity in him which is ravaged by a frump.

Socrates said that nobody ought to be in the company of beautiful persons. Gorgias, the Leontine, lived eighty years, and said that the reason he had all his faculties was that he never did anything solely for pleasure. Before the average man reaches fifty his intellect is a senile carcass. Men of talent lose their minds earlier, for they compose their iambics for money to bring to Venus. Archytas of Tarentum said that no more deadly plague than the pleasure of the body was inflicted on men by nature. Lycon, the peripatetic, came to Athens for an education, and he learned first of all what each streetwalker costs.

The mind is as easily thrown down as the senses. The Greeks said Eros was the son of Isis and Zephyrus, which proves that erotical love bends under the softest wind. Aristophanes informs us that Eros goes as far back as Chaos; Plato in the *Symposium* asserts that Eros has no father or mother.

Pleasure is intractable, and it is told that Semiramis, called the wild pigeon, was the first one to castrate women, because people are mad for what is new or dangerous. Men spend their lives swallowing anchovies, polypi, onions and plebeian carrots, which either make them diuretic, or give them the potencies of pigeons, who are said to require the longest time in their hymeneals.

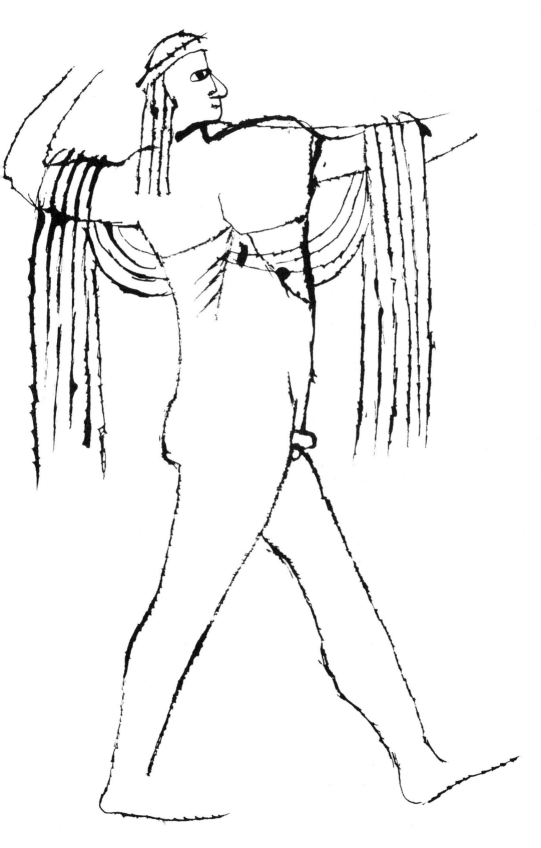

Man used to wipe his hands on the crumbs of bread and he was safe. Adam passed water and thought nothing of it. He defecated in a clump of leaves and had no lawless sensations. Now voiding is ecstatic and every one perishes for the stroke of a hand or a foot. One should wive an unsociable she-dragon, or a sloven who won't sit, or stand up, or lean, or lie down, for everything raises up a host of profligate longings.

A man may have the testicles of a newt, or wear the rugose coat of a she-frog to be repulsive, or persecute his gullet and abdomen to kill all desires until he weighs no more than one obol, but he is likely to be inflamed, attract a dowd, or have enough concupiscent skin to want a tittle more.

No matter how we long for virtue who wants to be a spado? Even the bull, just after he has been castrated, mounts the heifer once more showing that habit masters nature for at least one copulation. Nor should we give credit to the cold; Alexander never touched the daughters of Darius, because he had little inclination for women. Olympias, his mother, gave him the Thessalian courtesan, Callixene, hoping to cure him of his indifference toward woman, as she thought him to be quite impotent. After the sack of Troy each monarch returns home with a concubine, except Menelaus, who had wasted his genital powers in Asiatic orgies and so required none.

Why does this sadden the abstemious? Does it really matter whether a man can raise his pudendum or not? We are gluttons, greedy, inconstant, and wild asses, for no other cause than this ludicrous exercise. A legendary swan lives three hundred years, and a goose to be eighty, and though some only live long enough to be a goose, the longevity of the former would not diminish lust. What would the multitude do with a longer life except ask for a longer gullet or penis? All the feasts for Persephone, Daphne, Cybele, and the frantic, mystic shouting of *Hevoi*, which is the pagan Eve, or fornication, is nothing else but begging useless idols to give us the ability to rear up this ugly tyrant at the sight of any chit, girdle, or cestus. Since all is lost what harm can there be in a quick perusal of the whore's register of renowned Hellene?

There were Neaera and Phila who wore out her teeth in service, and Nais who had none; and Anticyra who only drank with crazy men. Glycera was the universal friend, and Nanium cheated her customers, for she was astonishing in her garments, but without them showed a listless navel and a brace of turnip legs. Phryne, who razed every husband to the ground, and put to the fire and sword his household, bore herself in public like a sibyl, only disrobing for the whole of Greece on the feast of Posidinia. Had she not observed all the holy days of Venus, that jealous goddess would have slain her, because there was no flesh under the moon to glut men like Phryne's. It is told that Lais of Corinth, who had kindled the fury of that deity, was beaten to death by a footstool in the fane of Aphrodite.

Olympia assuaged the rotten fever of Bion, the Philosopher; Theoris served Sophocles in his old age; Homer gives Phoenix as a mistress to the aged Nestor; Archippa, the heiress of his plays, lay with Sophocles when he was skull and wrinkles. Once when her former lover was asked where Archippa was, he replied, "Why, like the owls, she is sitting on the tombs."

Nicarete satisfied the bed of Stephanus the orator, and Metanira coupled with Lysias the Sophist, and both these courtesans were enemies of all mankind, one solacing an orator and the other a sophist. Philyra, Scione, Hippaphesia, Theocles, Ismathe, Lagisca, and Anthea forsook their occupations, after which time husbands became greater adulterers, going to other men's wives instead of harlots, and stealing out of windows in bags of chaff. This larded deceit, falsehood and cant, for nothing good ever comes of the virtue of a whore. Herodotus praises Naucratis for its beautiful wenches; it is said that Stilpon the philosopher had as his pupil Nicarete of Megara, but she should have confined her metaphysic to his sheets and pillows. Billisticha came from the house of Atreus, and her favors were dear. Leme could be had for two drachmas, and her name means the matter that gathers in the corners of the eyes, a poor name to be purchased for money.

But here is the wind in the paunch of Falstaff, and some filberts for Caliban. Consider the operations of the testicles; will you be Solon or tread a thousand whores and live to die senile? What is copulation that man should be tickled into dotage? Are we born solely because the red mullet and the sea perch have wombs? Shall we eat honey and locusts, or be Agrippina?

CHAPTER I

Man must be classed among the brutes, for he is still a very awkward and salacious biped. What shape he will assume in the future is vague. There are many traits of early man he has lost, and it is plain that he is much more given to falsehood, robbery and lawsuits than the primitive. The first two-legged man scratched himself because he had an itch. Men now lie and steal for this pleasure. Primeval natures wallowed without thought, but soon as men began thinking how pleasant it was to rub themselves and to have deliriums from mud, they employed their minds to achieve what paleolithic mankind did without being lascivious.

Men lie, not alone for profit, but to root in Circe's mire. No pigmy or cave-dweller wears more bizarre or dirty raiment than present-day man. He is often as offensive as the gland on the back of the Brazil peccary. He would rather tell a lie than the truth because his sole purpose is to be a grub.

He is the most ridiculous beast on the earth, and the reason for this is his mind and his pudendum. He sacks nations, or throws away his reason to see the petticoat of Aspasia or Helen empurpled by murex or the lichen at Madeira. The procreative organ in the camel is behind, but in man it is in front, and unless he is too fat to look over his belly, he pays more attention to this gibbous organ than to his arms, his talus, or anything else. He frequently forgets how his arms look, and is surprised to find a wen on his jaw, and he rarely knows whether his pupils are brown or ochreous, but he is always mindful of his testes hanging between his legs like folly.

In the *Book of Enoch* the scribe says that the first two-legged creatures had the private parts of great studs, and it may well be that Methuselah and Jared and Mahalalel were mountains and that from their middle hung hills which were their organs of generation. Otherwise, it is impossible for one to imagine how they could live for nine hundred years without wearing out their genitals. It is known that Og, King of Bashan, had an iron bedstead seven cubits long, and that the giants of Anak had six fingers.

Adam bare stones long before he begat Seth. Human life began as procreative mud, and later man was a shark with a human face. There was a human species with a lion's mouth and the legs of a giraffe, for anterior to the neolithic period diverse animals mingled. Many of our traits are found in the countenance of the bear and in the lip of the pard. The story that the pigmies were chased from the River Strymon by cranes is also a fable of our bird origin.

The old gods were ocean, rivers, animals, fish, birds; Noah was a fish, and Plato supposed that Oceanus was the father of Saturn, and there is as much natural history in this as mythology. Men and rivers are demigods and beasts; the Scamander is the river's mortal name; Zeus called the fierce water Xanthus; in the *Iliad* it is reported that the bird, said to be named *chalcis* by the gods, was Cymindis among men. This is the heroic conception of human fate.

Pleasure brings about the most violent transport in men, and of all the animals in the earth none is so brutish as man when he seeks the delirium of coition. Democritus of Abdera, unable to bear being stung by any female foot in sandals, or round skirt, was said to have plucked out his eyes. He was as mad as a boar for the shape of Venus; when the testicles of the boar are swollen he is at times so beside himself that he rubs them against a tree until he is castrated. The female deer hates copulation because the penis of the stag is as tough and spinous as a palm leaf; the pain the stag gives her is considerable but she cannot overcome her passion for him.

One marvels what man will do to have his skin scraped. Antony lay with Cleopatra at Daphne for this foolishness, and though he gave all his force to her, his delights were not as long as those of the ordinary fly. One cannot submit a little to sexual excitement without hankering after more such raptures. When birds are continent their testes are internal, but after sexual intercourse the penis is very conspicuous.

Whether man is more lecherous than the partridge is doubtful, but he is not as chaste as the raven, who bleeds from the eyes during coition. The man of sensibility is not satisfied with ordinary coupling; all the arts of Lais of Corinth cannot furnish his skin and veins with the infinite sensations he demands. Pain affords him infatuate happiness unknown to four-legged creatures. He is almost the only animal that cohabits at all times. With the exception of the pigeon, a bird which abstains only a few days in the year, man has the most lickerish tail of all beasts. This has made him very unruly, and double in his words and deeds. Unlike the elephant he has no seasons for his venery. This pachyderm, after impregnating the female, avoids this excitement for two years.

The elephant is an exemplary teacher. It is in many respects a rational animal, and repents of its anger, which is rare among men; when it kills its master, it grieves and sometimes starves to death. The dam suckles her young six years, and many elephants live as long as people. When an elephant is sick he is given wine to drink, and when he has an eye disease, these warm, friendly orbs are bathed in cow's milk. His wounds are healed by butter. These are the simples that the Homeric heroes gave to each other at Troy, and the poet of the *Iliad*, as well as Plato, would have paid the tenderest regard to this superior beast whose diet, medicines and habits are far better than those of the vast multitudes in the earth. The elephant, doubtless, was no less a monitor than the heifer which is so often seen beside the seated Buddha.

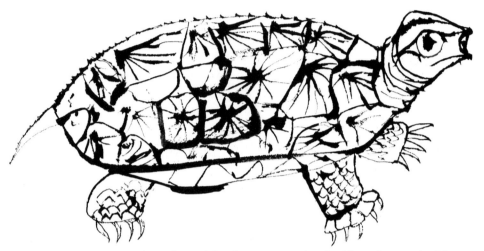

Countless adulteries are committed without lust, and with no thought to the peril which attends this folly. Animals do not give each other the pox; when men attempt to lie with a beast it rejects the malady that is said to be the companion of human genius. The adulterer is more senseless than the earthworm who keeps part of his tail in the hole he inhabits when copulating so he can disappear at once should he see an adversary. The tibulæ hide in the hedges all day, and seek the delights of the female at dusk.

Most people are furtive, but very few are ashamed; the elephant prefers to copulate near an obscure river bank, and the camel retires to the desert to rut. Modesty has been undermined because it is not generally known that the camel, more continent in his thoughts than a modern vestal, requires a whole day to complete such exercises.

Few labor for anything else but to exchange their sexual properties with blowsy dowds, or to rival the fox which has a bony penis: even the impotent are like the aged boar who waits for the tired female to lie down before he will risk his feeble appendage.

When the camel opens its mouth it looks like the greatest ass, though the ancients made the strongest bowstrings out of

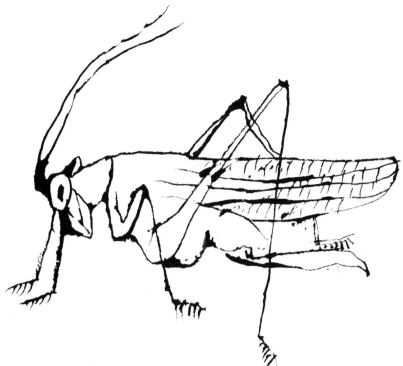

its pudendum. The egg of the *sepia* pretends to be black myrtle seeds; the vine the polypus deposits is its ovum.

The rhyades remain quiet until the equinox, and the grasshopper is said to sit upon the olive and reeds when it casts its skin, but man now stays in one place only long enough to void or feed. His irregular habits and haste make him the inferior of the polypi which unite only in winter, and these creatures conceal themselves for this reason for two months.

The tortoise gives a month to coition. The moose cannot have commerce with a red deer that is too short, but men and women of sundry sizes are suitable to each other. Andromache had too long a body, but not for Hector. Nubian dwarfs were ravishing morsels in Egypt. The pigmies who rode on the backs of partridges, which was a way of saying they were concupiscent, satisfied the giantesses of the Thermodon.

The puma never utters a cry when he mingles with the female. Bucks and does herd separately after the rutting season; man is incontinent whenever he has the occasion.

Men are more obscure to themselves than the elm or marine shells. The *solens* perish after they have been taken away from their borning place; the fir is comely in the sun, and the cedar is a Saul in the mountains. Man does not know 13 when he should plant, or from whom he can glean, or what town is his stony Medusa. The *sepia* deposit their ova near the river Thermodon, for its waters are warm and potable; the eels seek reedy ponds, and the pregnant red mullet lies among the rockweed. Paul the Fourth was an ascetic until his eightieth year, but when he became pope, he sported for hours at table as any mare in heat.

Men are too unstable to be just; they are crabbed because they have not passed water at the usual time, or testy because they have not been stroked or praised. The habits of animals can be ascertained better than the mien of a philosopher. When stags are bitten by the *phalangius* they eat crabs and are healed, but if a man has had a poor or dour sleep, he is waspish the whole day, and is likely to curse his parents.

There are certain fish that only breed in the Pontus, and many of the tunnies run to the Pillars to spawn. The *halcyon* appears only at the setting of the Pleiades and during the solstice. The crocodile is a modest brute whose penis and testicles are internal, and he could be regarded the peer of saints did he keep these members there. The polypus hides its ova in holes which is a lesson for modern women who, when they are with child, go through the streets showing the results of their shame. When the mare wants to sport with the stallion she makes water. But this lubricous mammal is continent compared with man, and he eats herbs, barley and oats which is a diet similar to the sacred table of Pythagoras. One has to travel to India to find a savant as herbivorous and savory as this extraordinary brute.

We scoff at Alexander for burying his horse Bucephalus, but the stone of that stallion shows that he had the separate toes of a human being, and this monument stands in front of the temple of Venus Genetrix. Bucephalus was so named because of the breadth of its head. Plato means wide forehead, and it is interesting to add that the philosopher came of the family of Hippias who were horsemen. The horse is so marvelous to behold that Semiramis was seized with the wildest passions when looking upon this carnal beast.

The horse goes mad pasturing by himself; separated from the human flock man loses his reason. Nietzsche, the wildest intellect of his century, lived in solitude, a Dionysiac disease which in crazy horses was known as the hippomania. In his last Bacchic throes he flung his insane arms about a horse standing in the gutters of Turin.

No one but a perverse person takes exception to horse manure. Droppings of many animals are more healthful than those of people. Human dung, except that of primitive races, is unclean. When the stag's horns are most perfect he has a very offensive odor; unlike man, who wears the same skin all his life, the stag casts his horns, the bird moults, and the despised python sloughs off his vile coat; man's despair is that he smells; he is garbed in the same skin until he rots in the tomb.

The Aztecs sold pots of human excrement for working their leather. Civilized nations regarded primitive man as a savory beast. The ancients, having the highest esteem for the offal of kine, said the oxen of the Sun were stalled near the Ocean where the seascum resembled dung.

Man imagines that because he stands on his legs he is intellectual, but the penguin is a biped who feeds until he can scarcely move; the bear too can stand up. Man's passion for disorder, upheaval and bedlam explains his greed. He attempts to prove that whatever man does is for his advantage. This is not true of him, and sometimes quadrupeds, generally reasonable, are demented or perverse. It is fabled that the mongoose breaks the eggs which the crocodile hatches in the mud though it does not eat them nor derive profit from this act. Man's neck is as long as Plutus: Solomon said, his eyes cannot be filled with seeing nor his ears with hearing. He is so bored that he seeks the naive existence of the sow. Having devoured all the experiences possible to the biped, he now wants to be primitive which he thinks is the same as being chaotic, torpid, or supine the whole day. Baudelaire asserted that he had the wildest desire to be aboriginal, because standing on two legs was too trivial and average for him. Man imagines that could he crawl again as an infant or as any brute in the field, he could recapture a primeval existence. Others are only content with the testicles of animals. Could man moult his skin as the bird its feathers, and have new flesh, he would be innocent. The stag casts his horns every year, and the horse may lose his hoof, but each acquires what he has shed. When the teeth or the hair of men decay, they do not grow the tusks they show whenever they desire sexual frenzies, or the hair that makes them prance and sport and neigh. Were it possible for man to shed his feet or his hands he could have a naive heart.

Man pines to live but cannot endure the days of his life. The learned, crouched over their inkpots, covet the customs of the savage who cohabits with a Lais or Aspasia of the Amazons whenever he pleases, or envy the panther. The poet wants to be an animal. "Submit, my heart, sleep the sleep of the brute," said Charles Baudelaire.

Men have more sorrow from their entrails than animals; except backward people or ancient races they have fewer rites pertaining to their ordure. They excrete when they are bored or want a savage pleasure. The father of Beatrice Cenci drew the close-stool over to the fireplace and voided in the presence of his wife and daughter.

The Mohammedan of the old order wipes his buttocks with his left hand since he uses the right one to handle food, plant vines, or to greet people. A Moslem woman can divorce a man with a reeking breath, a fault unknown among the natives of Otaheite. Modern man rushes to the water closet, and after the most summary ablutions, extends his hand to the first person he meets. The ancient Essenes had strict tenets regarding defecation and its burial in secret places. Man at present dungs in his own house and considers himself a delicate creature.

The anthropoid is arrogant, and when he finds a remedy for a malady that is the consequence of a cormorant throat he is elated. Tantalus can never eat or drink enough countries, rivers, or carcasses, and this gluttony is the cause of nearly all human woes.

When the sow has a certain disease, it goes to the mulberry for relief, and when the horse falls into a declining melancholy, the sound of the flute will assuage this fever for which men have found no nostrum. The river horse, after overeating, comes ashore and presses its hide against the sharp rushes until blood flows from a vein in the leg. When ill the stork sups upon marjoram; and stags also, in failing health, graze upon wild artichoke. The pigeon has exquisite revulsions, and at times disrelishes his table as much as men, and then turns to bay leaves for food.

Despite all the spital houses in the world, if a man suffers

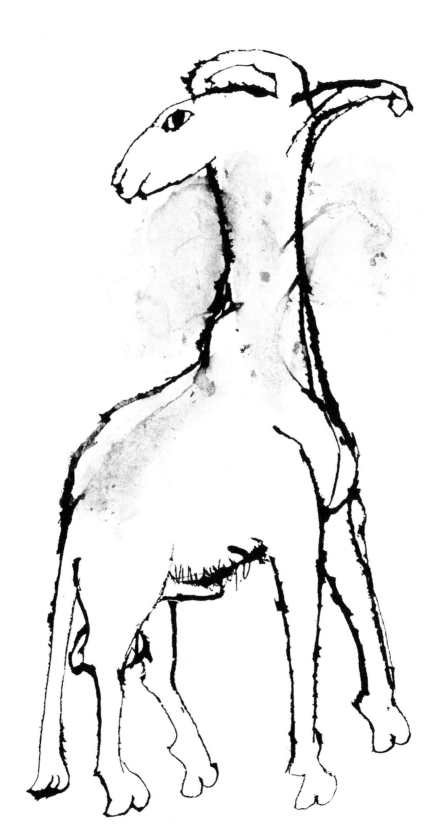

from strangury, can he do much more than the Sudanese who entreat their idols to let them urinate without difficulty. If it please Zeus may we pass water; to prevent chafing, if Cato be true, put a small branch of Pontic wormwood under the anus.

Socrates described love as the sting of a tarantula. We see that desire dominates the old as well as youth; the senile forget to button their clothes, and leave the door of their trousers ajar, showing what is no more than a relic of a quondam tower. Men lose their goatish powers long before their minds; Montaigne complained that when he was somewhere in his fifties he could not raise that sleepy animal more than three times a week.

The anthropoid is more luckless and unintelligent than animals, and the remedy for his ills is not progress, going forward, which is always to his grave, but turning backwards. He has extirpated most of the beasts which he no longer has as tutors. As a result he does not know whether to cohabit with woman, with man, or with sheep, and there are some who are enormously aroused by the sight of a mare. There is a breed of dog that will copulate with a wolf, and it is believed that a species of dog is derived from the tiger, and there is the Babylonian cameleopard; but, for the most part, the stallion seeks the female of its kind, and the elephant hankers after the same sort of animal that bore him.

Man is more incoherent than any beast in the earth. Schopenhauer has said that pleasure is the absence of pain, but it is not true. Man is not content with negative delights or even with positive transports. Some of his immoral deeds lacerate him, and he finds much satisfaction in being wounded. Man hates what he does, and that is what is moral in him, but he continues to do it, which is why he is Euripides, a spider, or the *Dryophis fulgida*. Man lies in ambush for all creatures, for he is the hunter; the Psalmist cries out that he is the turtledove about to be devoured by the multitude.

The whelp is most greedy for the soul that has fallen down to the ground. In the *Psalms* the soul flees to a hiding place in the mountains. The prophet rides upon a Cherub who is one of the fowls of the air. Man who is the master of the sheep and the oxen has the tender feet of the hind. He crouches before the bulls of Bashan and dreads man continually. But a little while he is a tree planted by the rivers of water, for all lurk in lairs to harm his branches.

Man is either too stupid or vain to know himself, and too self-loving to understand anyone. He cannot endure his own vices in others, and he is least just when he is railing at the faults of people.

Man is the tragic brute because he can never be as sure of others as the ass or the bull who knows that he is the booty of the wolf. A strong foe is better than a weak friend; the heron is always on guard against the eagle; the *anthus* is a reliable opponent of the horse since both covet the pasture. The deer when it has produced the fawn hides, for she knows what beast will hurt it. The wolf is the enemy of the ass, bull and fox; a mountain cat will embowel a porcupine; in a narrow defile the panther will leap upon a small dog instead of a human being. Men have no such certainties, and the more erudite they are the fewer companions they have. Aristotle in his old age said,"O my friends there is no friend."

Everything in man is double because he has testes. The old Nile god had the form of a man with a woman's breast wearing a cluster of water plants. The Egyptians extracted from the meanest worm the paint to design jars and the sacred, funeral amphoræ. In the time of the Pharaohs dense thickets were said to be the resort of malefactors. This was a proverb, and yet among the Quiché Mayans the gods were seated in the ravines, the forests and among the mosses. Not everyone that goes into the wilderness is Elijah or John.

If one considers the acts of his youth he wonders why he was ever young; or if he ponders his later vices he asks himself why he is still alive. In what manner is Messalina superior to the puma, or is anyone any better than a beetle which takes such pleasure in the fungus, called the English phallus, which has a most odious smell. The testicles of the American lizard give off a musky odor, and the monkeys in Brazil when stroked have as pleasant a scent as Alexander of Macedon. Priam had fifty bedchambers, and despite such opulent amorous experiences had no more sense than to select as his consort the termagant Hecuba. Solomon's bed linen was fragrant with Sheba and the perspiration of a hundred concubines, but were they any dearer to the nostrils than the musky testes of the lizard? There is a paradox: the Egyptians claimed that their land was infested with scorpions until it was settled by Apis. The serpent in Eden gave Eve knowledge of the phallus, and this is the source of art, science, poetry, wisdom, and perfidy.

We weep because the human race is no better than it is. The aquatic frog has the tail of a fish until he makes a twig or a blade of grass his house, then he loses his tail and grows legs. Nature advises the frog far better than man; a noddle endeavors to employ faculties he does not possess, and the eunuch burns for Jezebel.

Where is Apollo who rested his foot on the skull of an ox; where are the wild horses, the fawn, the roe, the cubs of bears that were brought to the altars of Artemis? Shall we wed, or woo, or tremble?

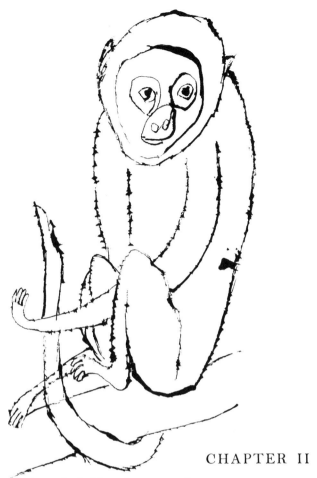

CHAPTER II

It is obvious that we must imitate the habits of many quadrupeds if we are to be gentler.

The animal is still crudely limned, and this is also true of viviparous man. Though he is the one mammal that thinks, the embalmers at Abydos passed his brain through the nostrils. He is much more inconstant than animals. The eyes of the goat and the stag are of one color, and only in men are those two unstable pools of various hues.

He is altogether a double nature, having two lips, two eyes, a pair of feet, and a right and left hand. Man is a congenital hypocrite because he asserts that his purpose is simple. Should he aspire to be apodal, at least, he would have no feet to hasten him to evil.

The pouch between his legs is divided into two, but it can never be asserted that one testicle is the adversary of the other, but the two have one sole purpose. No one then dare be a disciple of a hedonist for the simple reason that it is hard enough to accomplish any idea or good work so long as people have two limbs, two crooked lips and double eyes which devour whatever the mind considers a benefit to others and a deeper nourishment of one's own nature. It is better to try to be continent and to fail than to be an epicure. Antisthenes, the pupil of Socrates, said that when he had any sexual needs he took whatever there was at hand, a trull, a slut, a vendor of vegetables in the Agora, and that she was exceedingly grateful.

Man is double, and who may know his heart: he is a moral hermaphrodite. When Zeus was asleep he dropped his seed on the earth from which grew a demon with the genital organs of a man and a woman. The gods cut off the male organs of generation of this androgynous fury, which produced an almond tree. After the daughter of the river Sangarious ate the fruit of the almond she conceived and bore a son who was suckled by a he-goat. Concupiscence and force are the source of all our actions, Pascal wrote. We eat the almonds and conceive, and all our sons are reared by goats.

Most people are satisfied in shoals, their noon is night and shame, and their dreams are the garbage of their days; man fetches his dreams with the same fetid food he baits the purpuræ. All his members are arrogant; the hands, the feet are terrible tyrants.

Man is born wanton, wild, and asinine; he succumbs either to good fortune or to evil tidings, being the toady of both, because he does not know what to do with his head or fingers, or what his mind or hands can do well. The loon uses his sharp head to pierce the water, and his broad, palmated feet as oars. The *New Testament* is the gospel of the hands, and few can comprehend the homely adage about the tares and the wheat because they have not the manual intellects of the lowliest publican or carpenter in Bethlehem. The muleteer desires to be Virgil, and the goat licks the olive of Minerva which was said to render it sterile.

The human hand, though it is divided like the foot of the panther, can write, and tenderly touch a child or a mother. The hand, still a residual talon, and when meanly made more predatory than the claw of an eagle, is a marvel to behold. Ezekiel's four Cherubim have an ox in one cheek and an eagle in the other, and though they are feathered, they have human hands. Unloving hands are avaricious horns; unable to caress they are too puerile and deformed for morals or sensual delights.

The Coaita is a large Amazonian monkey; unlike human beings he confines his sojourn, dwelling in the valleys and uplands of the Amazons. His prehensile tail is as close to a human hand as the New World has produced among the higher forms of mammals. Hands in America are strong and cunning, but loveless.

It is abominable to have the same hands and feet throughout one's life, because there is so much vice and shame in the old hands. What cupidity there is in each finger, and in what unclean places have they been, and how often they skulk or hide in pockets because they are parsimonious or debauched. Men with women's hands are often preferred, but long, narrow fingers and nails are more suitable for malign ends than for affection.

Sometimes, the hands of men are the parables of the body. No lion, pard, pelican or heron has the head of Euripides, or Paracelsus, and one may surmise what a god was the occiput of Amos who was a gatherer of the Sycamore Fruits. The loins of the Angels are of burnished brass or of fire, and men when they are not hirsute are not entirely base. The ears of Aphrodite are small, rotund and toothsome, but the lobes of the male are a wallet into which he stuffs his greed, gossip, and carnal stupidity. Ears, often no better than the sow's, have a sluttish aspect; they root on the sides of the head, and like the pig can be fed mire and almost any filth.

The ears are worse than the navel because they cannot be hid. There are two kinds of ears, one which is a scale of justice in which all human pains are weighed, and there is the voluptuous ear which is a flute or a lyre, and which is always trembling; every man can play upon it, and receive some tune for his effort. One with fluted ears has eyes for wonders and marvels, and he is able to watch a poor man swallow stones and regard it more as a prodigy than a cause for pity.

The foot is far less wise and good than the hands or ears, and the toes are not so savory in aspect as the horse's hoof. Often human arms and feet are no better than the feet and fins of the cephalopod, and the mouth of the unintelligent is the

tubular siphon of a squid. It is said that man alone has a face, though if one goes abroad this statement is likely to be denied.

The dolichocephalic head is wonderful to behold, and one can have some certainties regarding the cranium of a great faculty. It is easier, however, to recognize the head of a pompion or a gross churl than to discern a wise head. Homer informs us that the head of Thersites is peaked at the top; Thersites employs scurrile words, and is always reviling Odysseus, or Agamemnon, or Achilles for no other reason than that they are superior to him in understanding.

There is no greater ruse than the human physiognomy; the eyes, the nose, and the hands are subtle snares, and the most practiced observer is not sure whether the genius of the person is in the general expression of the entire character, or whether it is to be viewed in the behavior of the neck, or the shape of the nose. He who relies on the testimony of his eyes is very likely to be duped. The character of a person is as much of a riddle as the substance of the soul or the Intelligence of the Universe. In the Cherubim of Ezekiel the ox in one cheek is the ruminative side of the face, and the eagle in the other signifies power. Frequently one sees only the predatory eagle, for men employ their force for booty rather than as angels.

There are countenances which at first blush look like wisdom, but upon closer acquaintance turn out to be vacant. This is particularly true of the large proboscis on the face. Most men of considerable intellectual strength have a conspicuous nose resembling a potato, a squill, a testiculate cucumber, for the nose is the second phallus in the male. Besides that, it is the messenger to the testes, for virile olfactories not only take much delight in the *Analects* of Socrates or in the *Dialogues* of Plato, but they also revel in good weather, inhale the seas and fruits, and are very quick to capture the fragrant skin of Nicarete of Megara or the adulterous uterus of Clytemnestra.

Agamemnon had a heavy rather than a strong nose, and he was a coarse rustic soldier with women, for warriors are not acute in amorous matters, and for this reason was of little worth to Clytemnestra.

The small nose is regarded as more comely in a man, and though it is handsome in a face at table, it generally goes with a short, miserable penis in bed. Lascivious women run after men who have a nose the length of the small finger, but are grievously disappointed when they cohabit with them.

Although the elephant uses its nostrils as a hand, it cannot be said that an animal has a nose, which is the sign of a higher creature. The nose is not entirely intellectual, and though it is better formed than the testes, it is a residual privy organ, and in the prehistoric age men very likely used their noses for erotical labors. Today the nose is more inclined to scent the female than the *Nichomachean Ethics*. As Aristotle remarks, it is good to take pleasure in the smell of apples, but it is intemperate to dote on unguents and incense.

Next comes the mouth which when open is as gawkish as the blowhole of a fish. So long as man has a tongue he cannot be likened to the feathered tribe or with the majority of mammals. What ascetic can compare with the grasshopper which has no mouth and lives on dew?

Man is the animal that talks, but the Cosmos is an Act, not a word. Thoth is the alphabet god, and he is the first month of the old Nile year when the funeral papyrus was placed in the hollow wooden figures of Osiris, between the legs of the deceased. Since words have fallen into disrepute we will either return to glyphs or to the simple neighing of the river horse.

The tongue is even less covered than the scrotum, and can hardly ever be called a secret part since few men have enough character to keep it in their mouths. It is difficult to know whether the tongue or the phallus is more harmful to men. The panther and the lion remain in their lair far longer than the tongue will stay in the mouth. This member is the foe to the whole of mankind. Hermes has empowered it with speech, and its utterances are sometimes oracles. Still, there is no galled tail so hurtful as this organ. It is a thorn, a stone, and also a witling, for when it is not a thong, it is a fool, and man spends the greater portion of his life reprehending himself because he could not be silent. If he has nothing to say, he speaks it, and sometimes this adder stings and poisons a friend, without cause and, particularly, to express ingratitude to one who has been kind or bestowed upon him a benefit. Even when it is hid in either jowl, it is a sly animal. Everyone is its prey, and as it is said in the *Book of Esdras*, "The stroke of the tongue breaketh the bones."

There is no other part of the body that is so busy; the secret parts in the middle are often lame, but the tongue is rarely dormant, or lying content in its cave except when it has made a huge boast, or has encountered another asp that can wound more, is quicker in guile, or in unjustly assorting words together. Silent people are more prudent than the garrulous, and, though their tongues think rather than speak, they are untrustworthy. As man is not very intelligent it takes him a long while to recognize either his foe or his patron, and he often praises the man who is preparing his ruin, and has an insolent face for one who would give him prodigal affections.

Litigations, courts, legal documents and countless laws have been spawned by the tongue. The tongue of the fish is thorny, but not free, and the sacred Nile crocodile has no tongue, though it devours men, but it is still a more enlightened creature than human beings, because men eat men, and have tongues. The bird is said to be able to put its tongue out as far as the width of four fingers, and that is a very dispiriting fact. The reason that the tongue is hidden in the mouth is that it can hardly be proud of its vile labors.

Far worse than the human nose, often well-made, and the tongue, are the testes, the most ugly and ill-shaped member. The phallus is a slovenly bag created without intellect or ontological purpose or design, and as long as the human being has this hanging worm appended to his middle, which is no good for anything except passing urine and getting a few, miserable irritations, for which he forsakes his mother, his father, and his friends, he will never comprehend the Cosmos. The *balagrus* are without ova or semen, but the Cherubim on the walls of the temple of Solomon were painted copulating.

The tail has grown weaker in apes and men. This is the fifth hand of both; it does as little climbing for some of the Cebides as it does for Pale Face. The scarlet-faced monkey inhabits the forest, and though it is never known to descend its short tail is no sign of terrestrial habits. Man, the fifth-handed climber, is weak; he is not among the branches, or on the ground, and where are the apples and olives of all flesh?

The phallus has always been considered an unkempt beast. Though matrons and virgins brought fillets and hyacinths to this rude, homely god, it was never his face, but rather his abilities that were worshipped. Ptolemy Philadelphus had a

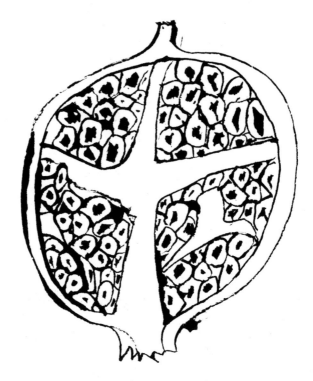

priapic image made that was one hundred and twenty-five cubits in length, and the effigy of this lewd brute was carried in the festivals either to Isis or to Osiris. Nearly every ancient idol was priapic. This was the god that protected the garden and seed-time, and who was associated with the melon, the leeks, the mandrake, and the apples of Haran which were aphrodisiacs. The onion was supposed to inflate the courage of the weak and the nervous. Hercules, the patron of the stoic, because he purged the Augean stables, and extirpated the robber Cacus, was at first commended because of his astonishing prowess in bed. This is not too likely. Giants are clumsy with Venus. One can hardly conceive of six-fingered Anaks as having amative wisdom. In neither the *Odyssey*, nor in the fragment of Euripides does Cyclops have any progeny. No women are seen in the monster's cave or island.

Man-eaters, giants, or the well-favored males have less skill with Aphrodite than gnomes or ugly men. Ovid asserts that cripples perform best. The Pythagoreans called lettuce the eunuch of the vegetables, and Adonis hid beneath a head of lettuce. Narcissus is an enervated lover; he is too vain to care for anybody, and so self-loving that he is not likely to have an erection, for nature will not allow anybody to get that excited about himself. He goes to a woman to have two admirers and not for other indecencies. Narcissus, or his Semitic forbear, Ham, has no shame, and the wisest and best men in the world are those who are ashamed. The conscience of Saint Augustine and Tolstoi came from their shameful parts.

Meanwhile, since man is not going to be different for a thousand milleniums he should select certain animals to teach him to be just, eat and gender at regular intervals, and blush. A learned nature never ceases to be revolted by his privy parts which remind him of his nose and his tongue, that second illicit organ of the human being.

When people have been lawless for a half a century, they cannot master themselves at all. Plato may say that the pentagram is a symbol of the good, but all Euclidean shapes and abstractions and Pythagorean diet are no more than the avoidance of the troublous testes. Besides this, what is known as the creative organ is droll and as foolish as the visage of a mule, or a thumb, or a navel, could they smile.

The prepuce is a fatuous appendage, and the entire tribe of pudenda and scroti have the heads of pigmies and the wrinkles of stupidity, decrepitude and mirth. This race, for the penis, despite the fact that it is attached to each person, has its own disposition; it goes where it will, and though the spurious owner wants to think, it wants to urinate, and if its helpless landlord desires to read or to sow grass, it wants to lie in bed; since it is only given to us as a loan or is leased to each one, man has little control over it. A man may want to study Mark, or Paracelsus, or go on an errand to do a kindness to an aged woman, but this tyrant wants to discharge itself either because the etesian gales are acerb or a wench has just stooped over to gather her laundry. The whole matter, when one thinks of it reasonably, is bizarre. The head is so obtuse as to go absolutely crazy over a pair of hunkers, which is no more than a chine of beef. Of course, the whole of human appetite is ridiculous, and although we are delighted to hear that after Ajax has returned from a furious battle with Hector, and has been lucky not to have been killed, Agamemnon gives him a leg of an ox as a reward. Naturally, Ajax is a very stupid man, but who is any better?

There is nothing more outlandish than the necessities of the scrotum and the anus. Lewd men are almost always eccentric; Charlemagne kept the prepuce of Jesus in a box at Chartres. Though good men often abhor their lascivious desires, the wether is also likely to be obscene; spados stood at the side of Phoenician Jezebel, who was a votary of Priapus; however, a eunuch came to the aid of the Prophet Jeremiah. Nothing can be foreseen because all men are unstable.

The saint cannot endure his skin; he is overthrown by his sense of smell, and pleasure lows in his ears all day. He is the prisoner of the least sound or touch; during the season of coition the male fish is in such a state of excitement that if the female strikes his abdomen with her mouth he has an orgasm. The voice of the locust is produced by rubbing himself with his legs. What an odious thought for the seminal male. Origen yearned to be a fish or an apodal animal which has no testicles; but eunuchs burn and fish have young.

We are residual beasts, and though the Cosmos inspires the deepest awe and prayer in mortals, this satyr between the legs is the crudest in shape, and the Creator could not have given serious thought in its making. The Ocean is our father, and the Earth our mother, but the penis is an afterthought.

The will is the deity in man, but it sows its seed in stony places; Philo has remarked that where gold and silver grow naturally, grass and fruit do not. When the will dwindles, the spirit stinks. By soft rivers and willows men lament and love, and small waters produce legends; capes, streams, and promontories take their names from Venus, Adonis, and Sarpedon, for whom Zeus wept; but Aspasia and Helen putrefy. After summer has left her cheeks can Paris or Menelaus understand why Ilium was burnt? The Ethiopic soldiers revolted against their king because he scorned their valor. Quitting family and homeland because fate nourishes the heroic faculties more than the household hearth, they rang their spears against their shields, and lifting their garments above their genitals, said that so long as they possessed such weapons they could secure a new country and other wives.

CHAPTER III

Riot, quiet, and surfeit are the consequence of sexual madness. Ten boars can easily tread a hundred sows, but this knowledge inflames the mind instead of pacifying the flagitious imaginations of men. The criminal joys of human beings are unknown to birds. There is no counterpart of Tiberius or of lascivious Messalina in the feathered races.

The great eagle has an iris of amber, and in appearance he is as vitreous as the topaz; this favorite of Jupiter was as regal and predatory as Heliogabalus, and the only difference between the bird and the emperor of Zeus is that the former will never touch carrion. The two Agrippinas, mothers of Nero and Caligula, were said to have had unnatural births, coming out of the womb feet first.

We go to the manners of birds, insects, quadrupeds, reptiles to comprehend mortals. Birds only couple in one way which has seldom been the ration of man. Ford Madox Ford, now among the woeful shades, rejoiced because swifts copulate on the wing. Every savant is a lewd goat or a sparrow of Venus.

Birds are reasonable creatures, and once we know whether they are insectivorous, nestle on trees, and how they copulate, their habits are as rigid as the laws of Numa. Numa Pompilius, Livy thought, was a wise legislator because he was an austere Sabine by birth and disposition, and not owing to any knowledge of Pythagorean discipline. Even predacious birds govern themselves in accordance with the laws of their nature, which they seldom transgress. Thucydides said that when the Median guests were slain by the Greeks, the ravens flew out of Peloponnesus; the carrion crow, the raven, the thievish jackdaw are great lawgivers. Man whether he is violent, or peaceable, is lawless.

The pheasant sleeps on trees to avoid the foxes; the partridge, dreading the attack of the polecat and stoat, avoids coverts. Man is either too obscure to himself, or he skulks in coppices and hedges to conceal his motives, which are not entirely reasonable, because his grandfather was a descendant of insolent mountaineers, or his mother came from the loins of Lot.

The duck is a constant social animal; he arrives after his vernal flight when the swamps thaw. The age of the young eider is the calendar of the Greenlander. The Indian hunting season was called the goose moon because this was the time when wild flocks of these species made their regular appearance.

Wagtails follow the plough which turns up the worms to nourish them; nose flies swarm in the nostrils of horses where they lay their eggs; but the rational human biped is hoodwinked every day of his life, and he is a more arrant misologist than he who has little or forlorn hope of ever being reasonable at any time with anybody.

The meat of wild duck and geese has the flavor of the bog; primitive morals too are as rank and plain as the forest or swamp. Savages are neither the artists of Eros, nor poets.

The bones of people are related to their morals, but who can know the rapacious. The feathers clothe the legs of the eagle as far as the pounces, but the talons of men are hidden. The raven weighs ten to twelve ounces, and is most cunning,

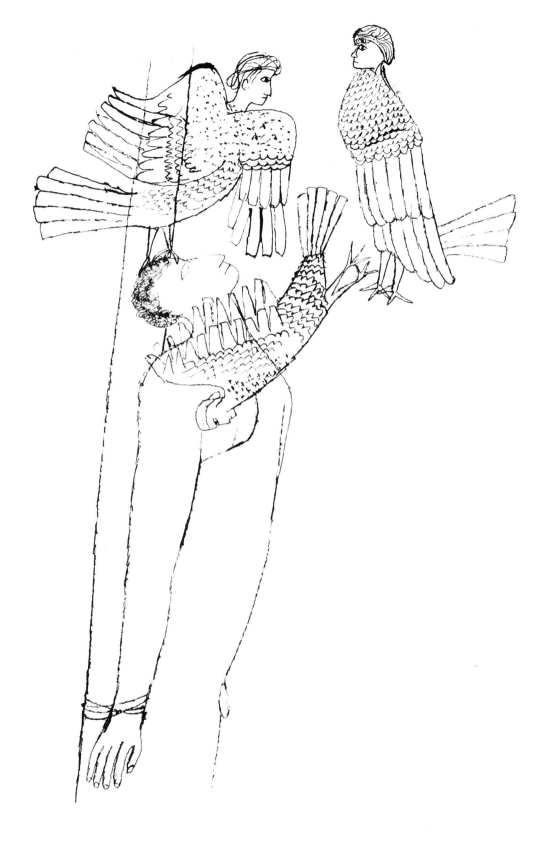

but can he compare in dimension and bulk with man? The percnopterus is a degenerate bird, but unlike the debauchee it has no agreeable traits to hide his character. White ernes ravage fawns, pigs and lambs; the fishy smell of the osprey discloses its booty. The osprey lives among the reeds, and the white erne builds its nest in the maple, the cypress, and in the pines; the solitary bald eagle nestles on the cliffs. Men live everywhere, marry anybody, and their prey are their friends.

Man is the most inconstant of companions. The pelican quits the river Strymon to incubate near the Ister; wild geese prefer icy Greenland. Each year the swallow goes to the aits on the Thames, and this regular habit is a proverb for the reed shaken in the wind. The widgeon takes her young on her back and flies to the marsh to avoid her foe the raven. Men scarce know how to scent an enemy or a friend. They smell pleasure rather than what is good, and like birds of prey have a cere which helps them to find their food. With this nostril of rapine man snuffs up the sophist, an iambic, the paintings of Zeuxis, the statuary of Polyclitus. He sees and hears as though he was always smelling rather than thinking. A just person, a kind nature, does not quicken this predatory cere. The odor of a good act, charity, friendship is much harder for the fowler to detect.

The scent in men is for hunting and selling; and a friend, as Socrates observed, is not to be caught as the hare is tracked. We must consult the gods, says the sage of Attica, to see whether they recommend a man as a friend. What incantations can we use or what sort of love potions concoct to charm a man into friendship? Socrates declared that he had friends who could not bear to leave him either day or night, and among these were Plato, Antisthenes, Aristippus, three sirens of wisdom.

The Antarctic petrel is a steadfast mate, and when one of a connubial pair is slain, the other ruefully dents the plumage of the corpse, pecking out an epitaph. If there is metempsychosis as Empedokles teaches, the albatross and the petrel are Thales and Anaxagoras.

Men show the smallest sense in choosing the earth they wish to sow or a suitable climate. Most of the North Americans dwell in sullen cities, and endure weather a Troglodyte in the desert would regard as unbearable. Cranes leave Scythia in winter and go to the Nile, and pelicans seek mild regions. Men are less sociable than panthers or the most rapacious wolves. Quails go in pairs and turtles in shoals, and the crow, the swan and the pelican desire companions. The solitary loses his ability to be with others, for whatever he does is for himself, which is wicked. He becomes very predacious and has a scorn for failure, and his madness for lucre is terrible. He canonizes the thief, the criminal, and simpers at justice, adultery, false-hood, and specious scales. His sole aim is itching and going some place else, and he has not the least regard for the difference between good and evil.

Who can dare give his heart to another without panting with fear; for his trust bleats in his bones. The albatross sports with the frigate, the dolphin, and the shark without filling the stomach of one of his companions, and this is a proverb. He is a corpulent rover of the seas, but his belly, when opened, contains nothing but mucilage, and is the envy of Seneca.

The cinereous petrels, found in cold latitudes, also neigh, and frolic together in the evenings under the poop of ships. Some have the albic hunkers for which men sigh, and their feathers are the down of the marriage bed.

Men go everywhere looking for companions, and do not know whether they have taken unto their bosom a viper or a crow. The eagle and dragon are reliable adversaries; ichneumons hunt the caterpillar; the lark and *chloreus* eat each other's eggs; geckoes and spiders are enemies. The *pipo* devours the young of the heron. The ass frequents thorny places; Aesop and La Fontaine understood this, but few others do.

The rooks live in communes in trees, but are continually tearing up each other's nests. The English rooks, though passionate and destructive, when building nests for their young, drop enough brushwood for the poor to pick up for their hearths. There are few houses that satisfy the mind or demonstrate parental love as much as the nest of an eider. The upper part of the nest is composed of marsh-plants, and the eggs are warmed by the down the dam has pulled from her own breast.

The noise of the turtledove brings the groom to the bride, but the song of friends has gone out of the land. Few have the genius for friendship; the many are dissemblers. The recluse sits on wild stones; the monk-raven, a hermit upon inaccessible cliffs, is a bird of filth. Let not the snail or ferret nest in your soul; shun the mole, it creeps and fouls the heart. The osprey, ossifrage and eagle roost upon the head crowned with tamarisk and rushes. Do not run after unguents which the bee despises; the carancros, American vultures, exhale musk though their food is carrion. The toad destroys the honey; the *rhine* assumes the color of the rocks around it.

Those who go by the name of Filch, Cheat or Doxy, strawed and cribbed best in foreign pockets, keep their purse-droppings to themselves. They are a solitary brood though guile and hypocrisy are vastly social. The feathered brigands often associate with one another, and their spoil is common property. The pilfering stares are the companions of crows, jackdaws, and redwings. The Troupiales of the Carolinas assemble in four to five coveys to attack a larger bird, and they maintain the same martial order as they devour the prey. The wisest of men fare worse than any feathered thief. Aged Euripides, having given Athens imperishable renown, lived more alone than a cormorant. The Prometheus of Aeschylus has no companions but the elements, and the eagle, his genius, which continually devours his liver. Men are consumed by their intellects, and what pard, jaguar, or osprey could bear to be so despoiled.

Men grow degenerate far from river banks and the bulrush, or lose their song or powers without the marine bivalve, but what fowl goes alone? All that man does is to rejoin the human flock. The widgeons fly together, and gabble with one another in pools as they crop grass or fish for crabs.

Most birds live in sylvan concord with those of their own genus; some do so until one of them learns that the other has different sexual properties. There were two birds, said to belong to the order of the Capuchon-Mordore because of their monkish cowl, who occupied the same cage. Eros had almost taught them to twine their bills which they would have done were it possible. When the younger bird nuzzled close to the older, the latter clapped its wings as the damsels of Israel sounded the timbrels. Desiring to nestle they commenced to weave chickweed in the gratings of the cage. When the young one began to show the raiment of sex, the other beat and continued to persecute it until it fell down as though dead. After they were separated each one went on to make a nest

which is the labor of both parents. Soon after they were apart the older bird died on a sudden, and shortly afterwards the young one perished from epilepsy.

Savages and birds are kinsmen; the birds of Mexico are the Chichimecas of the feathered tribes. The Aztec wore the saffron plumage of the parrot and the Xochitol, and these Mexican aborigines had as raucous a voice as that bird. The Tocolin is a brute of the forests who wears the imperial stole and breeches of Cyrus of Persia, but has no song.

The birds of New Spain wore the proud feathers coveted by the Amorite and Ashur, but they were either mute or dissonant warblers. Montezuma changed his apparel, which the parrot provided, four times a day, but he has left no hymns or poems. The canticles of the Quiché Maya and Aztecs are barbaric; Aramaic which Christ spoke resembles the wedges made by doves and gulls in sand and turf, one is the bird of Moloch and Venus, and the other belongs to the sea of Galilee, and both wear the poor coats of fishermen.

Before *Quetzalcoatl* gave the Chichimecas and Aztecs the precious corn seeds of Tula, they ate rushes and the seeds of flowers which is the food of the Tolocatzanatl. The thrush

37

swallows the haws of the juniper, which are so little changed when voided and dropped into the soil that they germinate. The thrush may be said to sow as he eats, but men feed without cause and gender at random.

The tops of turnips have been plucked from the craw of a ring dove and were so savory after they had been boiled as to be tender greens for the table. Would that the belly of men could provide us with such nourishment. The titlark is an artistic gourmet who will eat vermilion raisins before he will touch a white bunch of this fruit, though the latter is more succulent and sweeter. The stare haunts the reddest rose to seize the caterpillar; though he flutters about gibbets he is a mild insectivore.

The landrail is sluggish and abhors its wings, though it appears to be a disciple of Pythagoras. It is found in the corn-fields, clover and among the brakes, but its craw is filled with snails. Such food is not for a warrior or a thinker. The land-rail shuts its feathers when about to be taken rather than soar from the ground.

Each god, place, beauty was a bird, serpent, or animal. Paphos was the isle of Venus because it was filled with swans· Some of the rivers most precious to the mind were the Strymon, the Meander, the Cayster, the homes of this bird which represented love, hypochondria, and asceticism. Its food was often the marsh-plants and the algæ, to be seen on the banks of streams, and which bring lamentations to men.

The hierophants were called swans, and also those who were celibate recluses. Orpheus, the first poet, was related to this immaculate waterfowl, and gave up all connections with women. This infuriated the virgins and matrons of Thrace who tore his limbs apart and cast his lyre into the Hebrus. The head of Orpheus floated upon the waters to Lemnos just as the body of Osiris rolled upon the seas to Byblus. The swan is the bird of monody, and Milton, speaking of his oary feet, calls up the image of the boat of Charon.

The swan is a primeval voyager. Content with eels and frogs, a pallet of broken reeds, or with the roofless lakes of Siberia, or the Rio de la Plata, he has the hardihood for any anabasis. Wild and migratory he is Ulysses or Xenophon, but in water close by the dwellings of men, or penned in the gravel of a yard, he pines away. Who admires geese or cranes save when they darken the clouds? Ulysses, after he has returned to Penelope and his swine, is a corpulent fateless husband. Honeycomb is in exile, hellebore is home.

Helen, born of Leda, and the swan, is the most adept voluptuary of the palmated birds. Agamemnon traveled to as many foreign beds as Marco Polo journeyed to strange lands, but he was as useless to Clytemnestra as Menelaus was to Helen. Lust is the artist of beauty which was never wrought by a weak scrotum. These two sisters, Helen and Clytemnestra, pillaged Troy, sacked Menelaus, and murdered Agamemnon.

Swans are ferocious in their amours. The male swan begins by twining his neck around the female, and they remain folded together browsing upon each other's plumage until they reel. Ordinary passions come from grating, grunting, filing, sawing, flatulence, diarrhea, and catarrh, but breathing into one another's bill is Venus.

The female, once kindled, is beside herself and pursues the male swan everywhere, viewing any piece of water or clump of rushes as Solomon's bed and linen. It is told that she eats nettles to pacify her desires. The poets feign that the swan is a brutal river fowl, and that all who have that name are wicked; Cycnus, the son of Mars, was killed by Hercules because he was a robber; Cycnus, the son of Neptune, was slain by Achilles after he stabbed his mother, Philonome. The son of Apollo who had the same name was cruel. Swans would be mild were it not that birds have massive testicles.

The goose has not the genius of the swan. He takes less time to gender though the gander requires six geese. Among ducks the male organ of generation has a spiral shape and when it is agitated it looks as though it were an adder hanging out at the anus. The musk duck has the genitals of a Vulcan; the flavor of musk, which comes from the glands of the hunkers, arouses such senseless ardor in the drake that any hybrid or pimpled dowd among the ducks will gratify him. The duck is salacious and as desolate as Byron after Augusta has gratified him.

Don Juan burns with spleen when Astarte has exhausted him, or when she has not. After pairing the widgeon grays. The sheldrake languishes without sea salt, the mallard declines at moulting, and there is a white duck that is impotent. The drake moults shortly after mingling with the female, and at this time he paddles in the water among the mangroves at the risk of being eaten by a serpent or an alligator. The swan and the duck are not the gymnosophists of the feathered race, and they fall into as much of a passion for the fulvous neck of a female as men did to handle the bosom of Theodota.

Of all the animals man is the most easily deceived. If a goose perceives that the morning dew or rime has been brushed, he is wary. The Chinese as well as the Indians in Cuba swam in the lakes covering their heads with a calabash in which they caught the feet of the geese. The shoveler, teal, pochard, widgeon, or a domesticated drake are the Judases the fowler employs to trap wild ducks. These birds are uneasy even when they see a hut which the hunter has built to conceal himself.

There is as much to be learned from a plover, sheldrake, or an eider as from Socrates or the *Laws* of Plato. What is man that he should imagine he is more than a goose? Democritus of Abdera babbled as much as any duck.

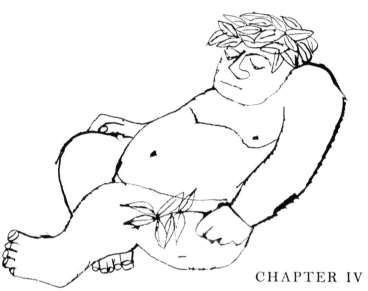

CHAPTER IV

Birds that live upon thorns do not eat worms or other living creatures, but man feeds upon everything. He is greedier for praise than the mullet and as voracious as the dolphin, and he is utterly blind to the motives of another. His food not only hurts the imagination but the affections. The Cynics carried their spare victuals in a small scrip.

It is reported that Menedemus used to give banquets to friends and passers-by, and that the second course consisted of lupines, pears, pomegranates and dried figs. This was an exceedingly moral symposium, and though there are wizened men and wights who feed as sparely, they do it solely to live longer without purpose or love or goodness.

Every sage has shown the greatest concern for what he puts into his mouth. Metrocles, the follower of Antisthenes, advised: "Gather lentils and beans, my friend." Cicero, a disciple of the teachings of the Stoa, did not eat until sundown at which time he retired to his house in the suburbs to have a meal, along with philosophic conversation with his friends. Xenophanes thought nothing so good as a meal of chickpeas, vetch and wine to ready one for talk.

Conversation is the most digestible victual; when a man talks well his friend is as responsible as he, for Aristotle, Plato, Thales, and Solon can be as empty as their companions, and nothing so exasperates a conversationalist as when his words are stupid and unwinged. Listless people can destroy the wisest faculty which is sociable, for the philosopher has the most energetic of heads, and as Aristotle says, the energy of friendship is the basis of society.

The Cynics were often observed washing leeks in a stream and preparing vetches. One Athenian was said to eat nothing but myrtle berries, and another was supposed to have received his food from the nymphs, and it is related that he ate so little he had no evacuations. What men should eat has perplexed man as much as any other enigma. Callimachus listed the various kinds of olives with as much understanding as Homer catalogued the Greek ships at Ilium, and a good olive is as epic as the best ship, and is likely to produce a better poet. A commonwealth of intelligent feeders will not be overcome easily; a Lacedaemonian supper consisted of kidney beans and dried figs, and these were often of more service to a Spartan than the javelin and buckler.

The old poets, too, gave a great deal of attention to food; and this was a subject of vast interest to the natural philosophers. Eubulus, the poet, said the Athenian men lived on air and the sweetest hopes, and this is utopian fare, for people whose bodies are dilapidated as a result of injurious eating and flatulent living are altogether squalid, and there is no morning in their complexions; they sit sick and stand diseased. The breeze that ripens the grape disquiets their bladders, and the sun that reddens the arbutus wearies them. When the poets have indolent minds the wine-gods are human casks and vats, and the stomach, as Diogenes declares, is the Charybdis of man.

Democritus held that honey is good to moisten the inward parts. A stiff dry man, whether he be ascetic or not, is as much of a bane as a boring water-drinker, and either is likely to drive the young as well as the middle-aged to more lunacies than the ecstatic conjugation of turtledoves, or the belly that is a hole that can never be filled. Who does not admire Cato who had the most severe tenets and yet drank freely.

It is told that the wine is the horse of Parnassus, and Hippocrates wrote that sweet wines do not make the head heavy; he also said that water flowing from high ground and hills is the best. Hippocrates, being a healer of men, used images that clear the mind, relax the bowels, and purge the mouth.

The mother of Euripides was a vendor of herbs, and many a poet came direct from the carts and wagons of the market place in Athens. Their bucolics and georgics were table diet and medicinal recipes. Books were in good health and were as gustable as parsley, onions, or pepper. Ariadne, the Cretan maid, when left on the shore alone, fed sea swallows, and this is the damsel whom the poets eulogized and dearly loved.

May has gone out of the soul of men. This month got her name from a concubine. A plain catalogue of vegetables and herbs was considered Attic verse. Aristophanes, as jocund as the trollop of May, did not regard such a ledger-book listing as a risk. He says: "Capers, pennyroyal, thyme, asparagus, garlic, radishes, sage and rue."

Isaeus, the Egyptian Sophist, was once asked what bird or fish was the best sort of eating, and he replied, "I have ceased to take these matters seriously, for I now know that I used to feed on the gardens of Tantalus." In the days of Romulus the Pelasgians set before the gods earthen dishes filled with spelt and coarse barley. The Greeks regarded barley as the most ancient grain which they offered as sacrifices to the deities. They used to bring barley groats to Delos.

Osiris and Father Liber taught men husbandry. When men observed that the oat cricket appeared at the time when the crops began to dry, they gathered the grain. Perseus planted the first peach tree at Memphis, and the savage, weaned from his foul repasts, became frugivorous. A moiety of his river knowledge came from the spider who weaves a thick web when the waters are about to rise.

Man's cruelest enemy is his appetite which makes him envious, inconstant, hostile. Human beings are the most restive of animals, and are in a worse state than the giant with

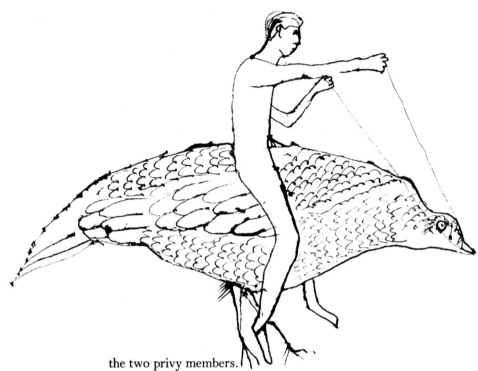

the two privy members.

The mind has increased greed and gluttony, and man's table proves that he is a manger, as Plato has remarked. The Psalmist says that man's life is brief, and yet he gives the least attention to food which is the cause of his early death. Pythagoras shunned the bean, and the lentil, and flesh, allowing his disciples fruits and herbs which would either banish dreams altogether or yield pure ones.

Human diet is foul because man eats what is available; a savage on the banks of the Niger has saner meals than civilized nations, and is content with the food, raiment, and wine of the palms; the Oritæ were fish eaters and wore the scales of those creatures.

One would imagine that man would have a low regard for himself because he has not learned to eat and void more sensibly, or to regulate his dreams. The spider drinks up the rank moisture of walls; but it is vile. The house cricket dotes on the scummings of kitchen pots, yeast and offal, which offend the imagination. The spider creeps up the tree at night to suck the eggs of the young of the hummingbird; it is loathsome. The wiles of the *Dryophis fulgida* are execrable; this pale, green snake has the same colors as the foliage of the Guajara bushes where it lurks to catch tree frogs and lizards.

A poor feeder, who is not a devotee of philosophy or has no passion for the *Georgics* or the *Compleat Angler*, is parsimonious, because he does not give himself to anything, either to an abundant meal or to a poet. If he eats badly, is not a fruit and grass feeder, we remark that all he does is to distend the bulk of his oesophagus. Animals feed, gender and sleep, but have not the wonder in their gills or feet or heads that Anaxagoras had. Plato tells us that the gentle when they descend to the underworld will be translated into bees, wasps and ants, but they are more social than we are, and have more ability for friendship. Man cannot scorn the hog, for, though he roots in the mud, he dotes on figs, acorns, millet, barley, wild pears, and neither gods, nor wise beasts, nor men find this fare intolerable. The tunny eats flesh, though for the most part he lives on seaweed, and in this respect he is as much of a seer as Daniel, who, in the Babylonian captivity, was content with pulse and water. This frugal diet prepared Daniel and his Hebrew companions for the furnace, and though friendship is a great trial and fire, few supply themselves with any viaticum for the perilous journey to another soul.

Plato counseled men to guard against the vices of eating, and I think he even urged people to shun fish which Aristotle thought was exceedingly fine food. Oysters are aphrodisiacs, and the dolphin is fierce, and it is possible that those that devour them acquire their traits. Since animals, clams, and polyps taught men whatever they know, the best we can do with the brains we have is to study the habits of these creatures in order to comprehend Plato.

Homer was in many ways of the mind of Socrates; the law-giver of the Muses hated Asiatic luxury, effeminacy, and stomach-love. Priam reproaches his sons for being "the wholesale murderers of lambs and kids." When Cyclops has no men to eat he diets on curds, cheese, and milk. Nestor cuts a slice of goat-milk cheese and an onion for wounded Machaon. Homer does not give Ajax or Achilles dainty foods.

There was an epicure who is said to have eaten his meat with fingerstalls so that his food would be as warm as possible by the time he had pushed it into his mouth. Aristoxenus of the same sect as Aristippus had a cured ham named after him, which is sham immortality. Melanthius asked the gods to give him the gullet of an ostrich in order that it might take his food a long time to pass from his neck. The greedy desire exquisite and mordant joys from every part of the body, and sometimes their arms madden them, and on other occasions they swoon because of the way they are housed in their clothes. Every pore in the skin of a hedonist is a voracious cranny, and this sieve of lust goes about like that sloven in Athens who always had enough obols to pay a chit, or a tart, should he happen to see one.

The infamous feeder is neither virtuous nor gentle, and the appetite of a gourmet is a bane; Claudius doted on mushrooms, which Agrippina poisoned to despatch him; a bad stomach is not good for wedlock, friendship, or philosophy. The aim is not to keep men from the table or bed or to pinch natural longings, but to caution others against the deliriums sharpened by Aphrodite. There is no reason to rouse the mad Muses in human beings, for man is already arrogant, lunatic, and impious, and requires no additional instruction in concupiscence. If he took greater care of his meals, he would marry better, and be, as one Attic poet has said, milder than the mallow.

Yet the gourmet enchants many persons; the sight of his gross, amiable belly warms the clothes of dwarfed souls, and his wines dispel the morose fogs that settle upon the solitary bones. Nearly every one is repelled by Christ, or wormy Lazarus, but few can resist drunken Silenus; the face flushed with myriads of flagons pipes in all blood. The horse, growing languorous after eating heated barley, resumes a healthier mane when he hears the sounds of a flute.

Men gulp their good deeds as well as their vices which are like the half-digested fish in the oesophagus of the cormorant. After people age and wax cowardly of soul, they sink into their bellies. Old Ulysses was a glutton and not better than the athlete Theogenes of Thasos who ate a whole bull by himself.

After Ulysses returns to plump Penelope he is porcine. Epaminondas, the Theban hero, said that no one ought to be so fat that he could not look over his belly to see where he was passing his water. The gods have no water trouble, nor are they gross feeders, and it is said that Apollo spurned envy, an unsociable deity. Man can never attain the vision in Plato's *Republic* so long as he is incontinent, overeats, and is covetous. Ulysses comes home to his pigs and wife at Ithaca to feed and wither; for when the battle of Troy is finished Ulysses is a stomach.

Fat people are oracles of wind and water, and too steamy to converse with and are not suitable companions for a philosopher's table. It is doubtful that they are of much use to their wives, for they are too heavy for honeyed mingling because their bellies get in the way of the parts they wish to employ.

CHAPTER V

The first mortals were content in swamp and reed. The herbs
of the marsh and dog's-tooth grass were bread. Sidon and
murex and Arabic alabaster were unknown. The seasons were
no more than a matter of winds. Men were plants and the
cowries of the shore, and woman a potherb, her legs and hair
were rain. River rushes, fennel stalk, the dusk were the odors
of apples and desire.

Salt pools were the eyes and head of man, his verteber was
a tidal seam; the marshes dreamed, the dunes thought; Ocean,
swamp and sands were in his mind and visage; he had no wish
to grasp them because he had no feet or hands, the malign
tutors of greed and strife. The small stones slept near him as
lambs. Sea and quagmire, kelp and cockle were mother and
father, and Abel, who is feeling.

Most enquiring minds are ever trying to learn how men
were in the beginning. They have the same elation that was

Alexander's when he saw crocodiles in the River Hydaspes and Egyptian beans in the Acesines, imagining he had discovered the source of the Nile. Paradise is what is First; Alpha, or Albic; the primeval mists, or the white stole of God. Aristophanes claimed there were at first three sexes, man, woman, and man-woman. This creature was round and he had eight limbs; his back and sides were a circle, and he had two faces. The monster had four ears and two privy members, and he rolled everywhere. He had no need to couple with another because he was altogether self-sufficient, although it is hard to understand how he connected his two parts. These androgynous creatures did not impregnate each other, but sowed their seed in the ground like grasshoppers. Having four ears, eight limbs, and two private parts made them fierce and arrogant, for it is doubtful whether any of the gods were so fortunate. Zeus decided to split the man-woman into two, for the giant with the double organs despised the gods, and had scorn for the universe and the animals in it. The brutes, too, before the days of Deucalion had titanic genitals, but these beasts were not hermaphrodites and could hardly rival the human giants. Zeus bade Apollo to reshape man, and he took the generative organs which were behind and put them in front, which was a cosmical error, for what man sees arouses him.

It was the belief of ancient annalists that men had far larger bodies than now, and that there were giants in the earth in the first days, when there was much more vapor, emptiness, and sea than earth. Nature then produced monstrous creatures that had the breasts, the neck and the head of men but whose lower parts were those of a sea creature. Theophrastus held that in the beginning man was a fish and like any other animal; the human infant was suckled at the breasts of the shark. Water came long before fire and stones. There were creatures also with the faces of huge fish that had one ear and an unparted lip and which lived by smelling potherbs and air. Saint Augustine reports that in his own time he saw on the shore of Utica a man's axle-tooth that was equal in size to a hundred of ours.

Nature created many monsters, some without mouths, others neckless. Hesiod affirms that there were webfooted men, and Saint Augustine writes that there were unipeds who slept under the shade of their foot. Strabo, Diodorus and Pliny were of the mind that there were people with baboon faces, and Augustine speaks of the Cynocephali that had dog's heads and barked. Nature was and is still at work on the shape of the races, and there is small doubt that men are dwindling in stature and in procreative strength. Homer sorrows over the depleted energies and size of man. Hector, Ajax and Nestor, who came long after the Deluge, were inferior to the first children of Adam.

Though there is a record of the first men in *Genesis*, they do not appear to have talked or gendered. Before Adam, man was in part stone, demon and brute. The Tree of Good and Evil bears the fruit of knowledge and shame. In Ezekiel this beautiful being has the round soles of a calf, proving that man is in greatest part a pure, visionary animal. Jared, Mahalalel and Methuselah begat without the assistance of the female, and these immense mastodons had no minds or privy organs, or any knowledge of their uses. Vice and coupling take a long time to understand, and though Adam and Eve preferred the Tree of Good and Evil to the fruits of infinite life, they showed themselves to one another without having sexual intercourse. Their great sin was in learning that they were naked, and this gave them boundless joy. Men learned to copulate from the angels that entered the daughters of men, and their issue were giants, who, being amorous beasts with human parts, were confused and stupid, because it is the mind in man that baffles the animal in him.

Woman was taken from Adam when he slept which shows that man and woman were originally one and that the greatest mistake that nature has committed was to divide man from woman, for what Adam originally had in himself he later had to pursue.

Unlike man at present, neither Methuselah nor Lamech wore out their parts in the first sixty years. There are many causes for the ebbing of human force in the earth: according to Philo, Cain was a profligate, and all malcontents are licentious. Human skin arouses lascivious aches, for the Greeks held that the original man was enclosed in a prickly bark.

At first man was mist and sea water, but as he was clothed with flesh he imagined he was beautiful, and it is said that Lamech, who was seventh from Adam, had a daughter, Naamah, which is interpreted as "beautiful pleasure." Pleasure came very soon into man's mind, and Methuselah and Mahalalel lived very long because they neither thought nor had lusts. Philo writes that Adam signified virgin red clay, and he partook of the Tree of Knowledge, or Lust, which bears the fruit of death. Knowledge brings confusion which begets lechery. Adam was virgin ground so long as he did not look at himself, but when he did, he grew shameful organs. Soon as man sees himself he waxes vain and desires to be a first cause. Adam did not mingle with woman until later, for it is said that before Seth was born he bare stones which is what the vestal earth does.

What is the ultimate form or the divine shape of future man? Augustine says that at Hippo there was one born with feet and hands like half moons. There are numerous hermaphrodites in the world, and we consider these nature's mischances, but they doubtless existed millions of years ago, and disappeared, and now on occasion appear again. There were persons who had both sexual properties, and according to Augustine, this double creature was able to beget children out of one body. Whether these are prodigies or marvelous births that are of the generation before the Flood we do not know.

It would appear bizarre to assert that man in the future will have no tongue, ears, mouth, or excrements, were there not fish and testacea who are the Seraphim men have imagined.

Man is unreasonable, and his sanity hangs by the thread of Ariadne. Doing wrong is one of his daintiest satisfactions, and harming another is as exquisite an ecstasy as coition. Man cannot endure his own vices in others, and he cannot overcome himself enough to pardon a friend whom he has injured. Proteus does not change his shape any more often than man or the earth which is primeval chaos. Human beings have not attained their ultimate shape, any more than the Cordilleras of Mexico and the Andes, which are unstable, fiery Vulcans, sterile summits, which in thousands of years will be ocean bottom where the race of Nereus will rove once more.

The human race has declining powers, and man resembles less the brute the more he approaches what we define as mind. He is in an intermediate form; the highest man will have no scrotum; it is ludicrous for a moral philosopher to scrape and

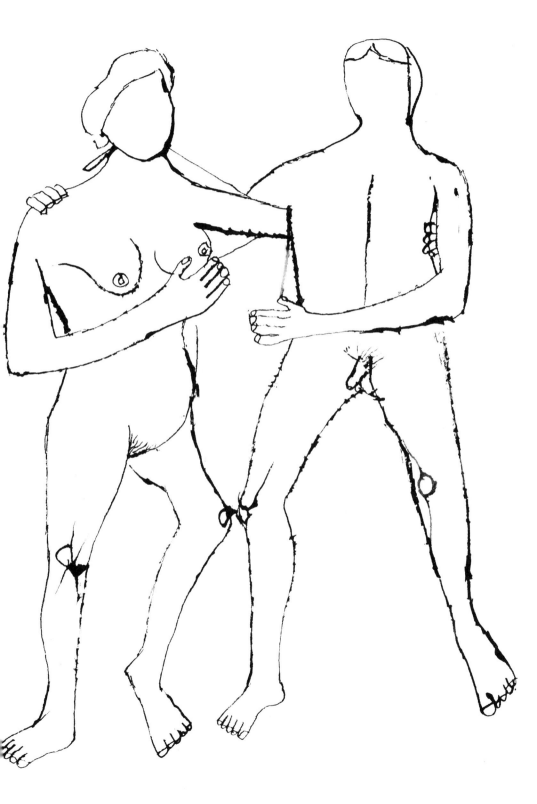

scratch as any worm. Euripides was a misogynist, but Sophocles said that though he hated women in his Tragedies, he found them rapturous creatures in his bed.

Man is at present in a misshapen stage, neither possessing the gentler customs of the beast, nor the faculties of the angel.

In some men the weasel is dominant, and in others the osprey, or the sloth, but he is weaker than most animals, and he is ruttish in all seasons.

Aborigines are the kinsmen of hills, larks, vales, woodlands; the kings of Alba bore the surname of Sylvius because the son of Ascanius was by chance born in the forests. Early in the annals of men the races are confounded; towns are of riffraff origin, and are spawned rather than formed. Romulus, desiring to gather enough people together for a Latin commonweal, set up a primitive sanctuary fenced round with briars and brambles to which thieves, the rabble, and violent fugitives from neighboring towns could repair as to a refuge.

It is impossible to predict the metamorphosis of human beings. Man in his present state has as much desire to urinate as he has to make vows to Artemis. He is still in a primeval condition, and is very inferior to the Mountain that spoke to Moses. Most of his knowledge is shared by the kite, and the shark and the spider. Though Lot was one of the last of the just men in Sodom, he lay with his two daughters and was as easily captured as the viper after drinking a vessel of wine left in a hedgerow by a hunter.

Lamech bare sons that were harpers, braziers and children who made tents of the hair's cloth of libertine goats; fullers and potters were lechers; Cain was a carpenter and the stones of his house fell upon him and killed him. Others say that blind Lamech, the father of artisans, slew Cain. There were also the women who worked at the spinning wheel who were lascivious, for they put their foot to the treadle, the motion of which kindles many secret passions. Penelope was a seamstress, and many of the poets of the Greek Comedy believed that she was unchaste. Dekker, much later, in recounting the profligates of London, mentions chapmen, maltmen, vintners.

God shrive the artisans Tubal-Cain, Gale and Garge, the patriarchs of the tambourine, corn grinder and the axe.

Only when the leek, the cucumber, onion, mushroom, and the Egyptian bean were cultivated did man come to carnal knowledge. This was after the Deluge when Ham was the first to observe his father's nakedness. Ham and his son Cush were the original artists, for painting is all about the nudity of other people and ourselves.

All flesh is trouble; if one bridles his feet and hands he is unable to tether his lips, and even when one avoids putrid food, he may smell. Every one in Athens shunned a pair of philosophical water-drinkers because of their bad odor.

In Eden there are two trees:"Behold, I have set before thy face life and death, good and evil: choose life." Every Prophet has perished, for if man eat of the Tree of Knowledge he will die, and the Angel with the flaming sword that guards the Tree of Life can never be overcome until men are of a different shape, substance, and mind. The fable reads that the men at Babel had one lip and a single voice, but that God confused them, giving them a double mouth, and many voices. Many stars will dim, and planets go to their doom, and oceans sorrow, before the human race can attain one sublime identity. When the two-headed animal that writes strays from the haunts of Artemis, the river gods, and the precincts of Thoth, he is the lawless goat.

THE MYTH GATHERERS

for WILLIAM CARLOS WILLIAMS:

William Carlos Williams, whose name is a token of his fidelity to place and whose perception is primordial genius, writes in IN THE AMERICAN GRAIN, *that the conquerors were overcome by the wild, vast weight of the continent.*

CHAPTER VI

Man is always seeking Eden, and the geographers of Paradise have named the rivers and located the blessed ground where Adam and Babylonian Gilgamesh dwelt. In the beginning there were cockle, scoriæ, sea lava; the onyx, jacinth, emerald of Elysium resemble Ecbatna, the summer site of Semiramis, rather than the primordial earth of the crustacea that inhabited the great waters. When nature wears scoriæ and igneous rock, she is the maiden, and her matrix is holy.

All men hunger for Alpha. Ptolemy titled *terra incognita,* Albion, which he imagined existed far beyond the Western Ocean. On his apocryphal map this was First Land, the immaculate continent, more suitable as the white stole of God than as cartography. The first shall be last, and the last shall be first is geologic scripture. The extinct, coastal bivalves which form the wet desolate cliffs of *Tierra del Fuego,* or the Straits of Magellan, more akin to Void than Eden, belong to what is first. In the beginning there was NO-THING before which the Angels fled.

Europeans came to the Americas for a new energy; Hercules had set up the Pillars as a barrier to the geographer and the soul. The Atlantic was the Sea of Darkness, and he who went over these watery plains had as his pilot, Charon.

Man is a dropsical animal, more water, sleep and death than any other element. Water is the lodestar of man; the Ocean contains seers we know not. In the seas all philosophies are writ; 'tis an empty bosom the fool may aver, but of such folly was the world created.

Of pelagic origin we are the children of bays and rivers, and Ocean draws more sighs and vaster ruins than the stars. The geographer cannot slake his soul at home; sea water kills the drinker, but not his fate; of marine salt is destiny wrought.

Orphans of Tyre and Utica, man-slaying skalds from the Hebrides, the Norsemen ranged icy Blacksark and tread the Virginia humus in beast's shoes and untied latchets, howling for threshold and kindred. They were a race of castaway Cains; a freebooter was Thorfinn the skull-killer; Eric was sent out from *Haukadal* to *Nod*; witch and bed was Thorbiorg, gloved in catskin; from the loins of Gudrid issued Iceland; the walrus tusk garnished her knife; an Arctic fox was Freydis; her breasts gave suck to swords. The hill, ravine and hummock were their book of lineage; the Chickahominy waters sired the savage; in the River *Panuncks* flowed his name; maize, gourds, squash, pumpkins familied the Indian. Each reed or osier was Abel or Seth to seafaring waif, widow or Indian vestal. Iceland is honest saga and farmstead; *Vinland* is the polar grape of Jericho, but Greenland, a tumulus in the sea, is Red Eric's fable and perjury.

The realm of Florida went as far north as the imaginary, congealed gates to Cathay. Cabot was supposed to have viewed this land when he was off the headlands of Labrador. Mariners have asserted that a Floridian bay flowed inland for three hundred leagues, and was a sporting ground for whales.

The Atlantic voyager was a gatherer of havoc; greed was his polestar, but his watery roots were his unknown quest. Florida was the empery of the Conquistador. This region extended from the land of Cod south to Powhatan's Virginia, and included Carolina, Georgia, Alabama, and as far west as

the fatal river-grave of De Soto, and the *Rio Palmas,* which is the *Rio Grande* River.

The booty of the Spanish was the discovery of a new earth, the annals of which are our legends and gospels. Small worth to them were the sweet acorns of the oak in the desert of Cíbola, which when pounded was Indian bread. What profit had Solomon of his wisdom, or they in learning that between *Sonora* and *Suya* the natives drank wine made of a great thistle, and that watercress grew in the springs in the wilds of *Chichilticalli,* or that the ravined riverbanks were heavy with pennyroyal, marjoram and a fruit, kindred to the rose bush, which had the odor of muscated grapes.

The European succumbed to the new continent; it was sterile earth which brewed fatal ends. Indian earth was a negative Golgotha. Martina Carvalho, a Portugal, went with over two hundred men in quest of gold which is almost as indestructible as avarice. They came upon a crystal mountain, and then saw a river between two mountains which shone like the stones of Ophir. They bit the grains with their teeth to determine whether it was a precious metal. In desert country their sustenance was some grass; one day they caught a snake upon which they supped. Sick and fearful of the red savages, they turned back in canoes, going on the river *Cricare*; in a rapid, the canoe containing the gold was lost. After eight months of starvation, they returned to *Porto Seguro* utterly poor, their hopes dead.

The Spanish hidalgo and Portugal adventurer came for riches, but the harvest was often no more than the piñon nut, tanned hides of the woolly cattle of the Platte, or virgin discovery, which, like learning, is tombstone destiny.

Ginger, cassia, storax paint the Moluccas in the blood, but Magellan's men are glyphed bones at the Popinjays. Gathering wrack in the windy Magellans, the sole lodestar of sea-worn hearts was their daughters at Cadiz, and entering a wild tract of water, named it the Strait of the Eleven Thousand Virgins.

Beneath the crust of the Christian was the new earth and river heathen. The explorers found feral ground that slaked their own natures. One ransacking customs to understand man is no less baffled than Montezuma was when seeing Cortes and his soldiers kneeling to the Rood, asked why they humbled themselves before an ordinary tree.

There were many martyrs of Canada and Florida, and the streams and towns that bear their names seem as legendary as the numerous towns of Jason that are everywhere in Armenia and in Media. The sea brigands who drowned in the Florida tides or in the Iroquois wilderness are as renowned as Juba, Ptolemy and Aristotle; they were no worse than Jason who was said by some to have gone far up the Ister, or even into the Exterior Sea. The Argonautic expedition was no less real than the fleets of Cristóbal Colon, or Sir Walter Raleigh's quest for the Elysian plains in Brazil.

The corsairs of Jason who learned navigation from Aeolus came to America for the Golden Fleece, but most of them died mad or drowned in storms off the Bahamas. Magellan, bringing the Christian cross to the Moluccas, was a lunatic pirate; Frobisher was as covetous as Cacus whom Hercules subdued.

The Spanish *Caballero* had an indomitable character, and good or evil, that is the ore of Prometheus and myth-gatherers. De Soto's men, steeped in the gall and hyssop of the American forest, made saddles out of the ash tree, and they cut off the noses and hands of Indians because war and bloodshed were their main entertainments. After three years in the wilderness, De Soto's remains were lowered in the hollow of a tree bark into the waters of the Mississippi. His goods, sold at public outcry, consisted of five Indian slaves, three horses, and seven hundred swine. Cortes had pillaged ancient Aztec sepulchres for gold. But all this was to be, no matter who the discoverers were. When the Portugals came to the Azores, meaning goshawks, the birds had no fear of men whom they had never seen. The Indians, for the same reason, were no less hospitable. This is the way of man, and neither Solomon nor Aristotle has changed him. The Spaniards, disciples of Ptolemy, Pliny and Marco Polo, could be no better than humanity. They were amazing geographers, and they left chronicles, bought at the price of an entire race, which is leafy and perishable, but history is not. In the fifteenth century there were maps of the entire earth carved in brass and pewter that were as wondrous as Achilles' shield. Centuries earlier Charlemagne sat at a silver table upon which the world was engraved.

The land is still unclaimed and unsettled, and the wild ground waits for the mattock and the hoe, and the love, which is genius, to make it an epic furrow, house and hearth.

Our forefathers were giant volcano-horses; America was hot earth as the elephant-shaped mounds in Kansas show. The great, grassy basin, the Catskill eagle made us tribal and fierce; the Pawnee, leading the sorrel of the Platte by a bull-hide rope, lessoned us in poverty, for Want is a tough, rude god made out of dried buffalo skin, to which we must kneel and pray, lest we perish of sloth and satiety. Men are milder on their knees, but ever chaffering with doom, grimaced by chance. We have lost the ground, city-cursed that we are, left it behind us like the *Quiché* did the *Yaqui* for whom they wept.

Return to the Platte, the bison, the hoofprints of the deer, for we are as hungry for them as the wandering *Quiché*, who had to smell the points of their *Ceiba* staffs to deceive their empty stomachs.

Whatever we do is vast, unconscious geography; we are huge giants of the mesa. The prairie is still an altar for the coyote and Ishmael.

CHAPTER VII

The Alpheus no longer contents the mind; when the sheep
drink of the waters of the Cephisus they turn white; it is told
that mares pastured by the Astaces which is on the Black Sea
suckle their foals with jetty milk. The mind sorrows and frets
as much as corrupt flesh, and neither ancient prodigies can
satisfy the one any more than Helen or Dido or Medea can
ease or keep quiet the other. Nature takes its revenge upon
the intellect because the body cannot rest; the intellect can
only quell matter in different places and worlds, or tutor the
feet when disease and dotage confine restive man.

All the errors concerning the human race come from not
realizing that man is merely another animal. There is no
beast as bored as man; tedium is his worst affliction, and the
root of nearly all his amusements. He is valorous in sorrow,
and the reason that he is most resolute in war and during
plagues is that he has a negative genius.

Let no one assume that the fables of the red races of the three Americas do not invigorate the intellect. The legends are vast energies to be domesticated; the continent is a prone mongol Titan, with the jaw of Osiris.

The minds of men differ little from the estuaries, the ravine stones, the fens near where they dwell. Savage ground bears men of water and stone. The Navajo said that the first man came out of the ground as a moth-worm. The Inca said the moon appeared first at *Lake Titicaca*. The holy mountain of *Tonacatepec* was the source of all the rivers of the earth. The *Witchita* mountains were the progenitor of the tribe of that name. The Egyptians say that the swamp fathered men in the beginning, and that they ate bread made of a bog root. Murex is found on the rocks at Gaetulia, and it is said that scorpions cannot live at Clupea. There is the forest intellect, and the mind sown by ocean winds. Some people have water souls, and are fisher- or boatmen, and they handle the oar. Other persons are tubers, or rough laurel flowers. Each has as his muse a tree, rain, or the humid leaves.

The American intellect is a placeless hunter. It is a negative faculty which devours rather than quiets the heart. *Dakotah* is an Indian word for friend though it is a cruel tribe. This is a battle and prairie mind. Its deity is not Christ, but *Quetzalcoatl*, who is wind and snake; and its travail is as fierce as that of the Indian woman who cannot bring forth until she is given the blood of the serpent.

The Indian, or American mind, is primal rather than domestic because it is new; the circle was known to the North American savages; the *Quiché Maya* in the *Chilam Balam* tell of the Father of the Kosmos grasping in his hand a stone sphere which set the four winds in motion. One of the gifts of Montezuma to Hernando Cortes was two round emblems in gold and silver representing the sun and the moon, but the wagon or wheel was lost long before the Tolteca and the Inca.

The American fable is a table of the seasons, the moons, days and annals of the pilgrimages of tribes. The Aztecs lamented their separation from *Tulan* so bountiful in maize, gourds, flowers and cacao, but their gods had no concern with human fate, or for the wounds that come from perfidy, chance, or from the decay of symbols.

Whether the lore of the Americas is as antique as Isis,

which means ancient, is in great doubt. Indian myths are the dregs of Asian lore; Greek legends are no more than Nile debris; the Arcadians claimed to be older than the moon, but how ancient are the red races? The *Muyscas* say that they inhabited South America before the moon accompanied the earth; the Semitic races wandered as far as the mouth of the Indus, and yet this does not resolve the enigma of the red-skinned children. The Indians of the Middle America have a strong Pacific nature, and yet *Quetzalcoatl* or *Kukulcan* was not a Mongol, but fair of skin, and bearded. These were few in numbers compared to the hordes that came from Siberia or the countries of the Scythæ or Tartars; they were flat of brow, the mouth of savage will, the eyes of China, but the jaw was European.

These new people, scorified remnants of Tartary and Tibet, had a jaguar *Genesis*. The Quiché Maya call their books *Chilam Balam*, or the Scriptures of the Jaguar Priest, and this is barbaric awe and theogony. Baal is a Phoenician idol, and a god of the Mayans. Aristotle relates that so many people from Carthage, who had formerly come from Sidon and Tyre, had departed for a continent beyond the Pillars, that a rigorous law was passed to prevent these Phoenicians from leaving and depopulating their homeland.

Diverse continents gender dissimilar intellectual properties; and the *Chilam Balam* of the Quiché Maya is a beast psalm; the Egyptian *Book of the Dead*, the *Gilgamesh Epic*, and the fables of the Aztec and Quiché Maya were conceived in the head of the crocodile, the bull of Ashur and the American coyote. But the papyrus lying between the knees of a Pharaoh, laden with mumia and honey, contained vows and affections not to be found in the rituals of the New World.

It is the works and produce of nature in America and not of man at which we marvel. The rituals of the table, the bed, and the hearth were never established; the naphtha that flows wild from South American rocks was burnt in the lamps at Genoa; Medea, lacking the knowledge of the turtledoves of Mylitta or Ashtoreth, destroyed her rival, the daughter of Creon, in the flames of naphtha.

Man is at the nadir of his strength when the earth, the seas, the mountains are not in him, for without them his soul is unsourced, and he has no images by which to abide.

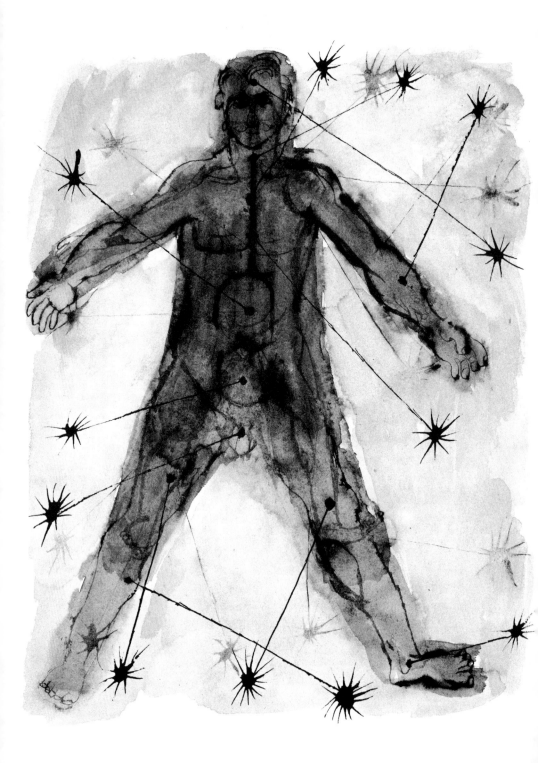

Much of the Americas was dead ground. The mountains about the Strait of Magellan are hopeless land; close by is Port Famine, and St. Julian, another fatal harbor, is a scaffold in the minds of men. The Strait is cool in summer, where wild horses graze on fungus. *Tierra del Fuego* is miserable, rainy coast though called the land of fire. The wretched Patagonian shingle was formed of extinct shells that were several millennia ago crustacea on the floors of the sea. The savages of this region live on the fungus and the berries from the humpback arbute, and eat the old women when there is a poor harvest of these outcast roots and fruit. Northern Siberia is frozen country, and the islands lying in the near-by sea are composed of the carcasses of elephants and rhinoceroses. These congealed, pachydermatous islets are memorials of torrid heat, the summer olive and the parrot. We underestimate the dead, who bequeath to us their sorrows and knowledge, and also their bodies. Lichen may be seen sprouting on a mule's bones. How long is it between the Patagonian fungi, the wild celery whose furrow is a bald cairn of shellfish, and the warm grass of Guatemala that mothered maize?

Maize, like the fig of Asia Minor, or the fragrant rice fields of Ceylon, is a tutored stalk of civilized peoples. *Quetzalcoatl* instructed the Aztecs to offer hyacinths and copal to their idols instead of human flesh.

The *Orinoco*, the *Rio Negro* and Indian land are not to be mistaken for the holy Pison; Sir Walter Raleigh sought the carbuncles, emeralds, and the gold of Eden in the woody swamps of the *Muyscas* rumored to be *El Dorado*. The rocks of St. Paul, though they be as white as the Angel Uriel or the stars, owe their immaculate stole to the dung of sea fowls. The sea slug feeds on kelp in shoaly water, but who will address this creature as Poseidon?

Man is still a rude geologist, and knows as little of the entrails of the earth as he does of man. Diodorus assures us that the Atlantides had no knowledge of the uses of corn because they were already a remote people before Osiris had taught the Egyptians how to plant the barley, oats, and corn seeds. The ancient Jews claim that the original groats in the ground were a particle of God's body. *Quetzalcoatl* taught the Mexicans the uses of maize, but this Caucasian hero, shipwrecked on the sunrise slopes of Mexico, lost his own memory; the lava craters of the Mexican *Cordilleras*, the pillars of cactus, and the thorny mimosas were far from the Mount of Olives and the Gardens of Galilee.

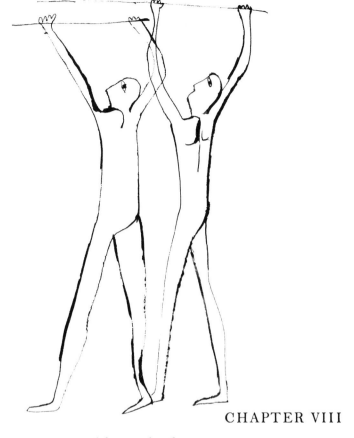

CHAPTER VIII

The ancient Mexicans were a gross lake people; they were
water sorcerers. Mud and reeds was their place of habitation,
and water made them as deceitful and brutish as the *Chichi-
mecans* who plucked up trees as though they were lettuce
stalks. Their idol *Vitzliputzli* made them wanderers.

The first tribes that arrived in New Spain came from the
Seven Caves; they were the *Chichimecas* who were Cyclops,
the *Ottomies*, the *Navatalcas* who had a polite speech, and the
Suchimilcos who were seeded by flowers and inhabited the
banks of the lakes; the *Tepanecans* had a *curaca* named after an
ant's nest which is found in huge, moist hillocks. Then came
the *Tlalluicans*, a rude tribe of the Sierra whose lord was
Quahunachua, now Cuernavaca. The men of bread were the
Tlascaltecans who built *Tlascala*. Those from the Seventh Cave
were the Mexicans who carried *Vitzliputzli* in a coffer of reeds.
This idol promised the Mexican wanderers copal, the balsam

of the vineyards of Engedi, silver, gold, turquoise, and the feathers of the macaw as their raiment. They came to *Mechovacan* which breeds many lakes and abundant fish, where they built a house for *Vitzliputzli*, and sowed Indian wheat and pulse. Of the Seven Cave nations, they were the last to people cities and sow maize.

Mamre is known as the vale of tears because Adam wept there, but the Valley of Mexico is the place of the skulls. The passions of nations would lead them to the *Psalter*, or to that vast plain watered by the Jordan and canonized by the bones of Job, were it not that man is mad.

The amorous apples of Haran did not grow on the Mexican lava hills and slopes of Scoriæ. Mire was their home, water their hope and desolation. The Mexicans left a remnant of their tribe at *Malinalco* because they were crones and wizards. They longed to dwell among the reeds in *Tula*, but *Vitzliputzli* forbade it. They changed the course of a great river so that it coiled around *Coatepec*, a small hill, forming a lake that nurses savines, willows, elms, and many fish. Their god commanded them to leave *Tula*, and those who did not obey the idol were found dead in the morning; their stomachs had been opened, and the hearts pulled out of the corpses. This was the labor of *Vitzliputzli* who from that time demanded human sacrifice of the Mexicans.

Copil was the son of the Mexican hag of the Muses, Malinalco, for art is sorcery. He was slain and cast into *Lake Acopilco*, and out of his heart leaped the cactus sword, the bloody plant of Montezuma and Mexi, the lord of the hordes from whom the Mexicans derived their name. The intellect is a bird of rapine; Philo regarded the angels as a sign of contemplation; the cherubim of Ezekiel are great winged birds of thought. The intellect in the New World is the eagle, and the Muses are wild earth. *Tenochtitlan* was built upon a stone where the cactus sprouts and the eagle sits.

The lake in which *Tenochtitlan* stood was sloughy and malodorous, and the Mexicans were in sore need of water to drink. After Autzol, their eighth king, was elected, he called one of his soothsayers to alter the course of a river so that it would enter the city. Manco Capac had cast a hollow cane into a channel to make the water flow, and Moses hurled the bough of an almond into the brook called Mareh, the Hebrew word for bitter waters, after which it was sweet and potable. Only the profane are indifferent to the rivers in the earth, which slake the thirst of the cosmographer.

When the bed of the great stream had been bent so that it brought a current of clear water into the Mexican lake, the wizards cast incense on its banks, sacrificed quails, and sounded coronets.

The names of the Mexican kings, and their lineage are a register of their customs. Their origins were plain and strong, for as Thucydides remarks, a people in their beginnings show remarkable energy; what often repels us is not entirely wicked, since everything that man does, when recollected, is a marvelous legend.

The original towns were of wattled mud and weeds, and their first king was Acamapixtli, which is the Mexican name for a few reeds. The one who succeeded him was called Rich Feathers, or Vitzilovitli. Of the tail and wing of the parrot and the macaw they wrought garments of as many colors as Joseph's coat. Birds were Indian gods and seasons; there were tame ravens in a temple on the California coast, and in the equinoctial lands the macaw represented summer and the raven winter. The flesh of the parrot was a Mexican table delicacy, and the aboriginal Aztecs ate mountain cats, tigers, and the puma which has the flavor of veal. When Cortes came to *Tenochtitlan* a small breed of dog was not only an immense delight to the Indians, but the Spaniards considered this animal as savory as a pheasant. It takes a savage as long to become civilized as it does a European from Toledo or the River Europas to become a rank thinker and feeder.

They also had Chimalpopoca for king, which means a Flaming Target, and then Izcoalt whose ancestor was a snake. When they elected a new king they drew blood from his ears and legs with the talons of a griffin, and they anointed him with the unction of the dead; some of the tribes derived their ointment from the oil of salamanders and vipers.

The last free king of the Mexicans was Montezuma, who told Cortes, his conqueror, that he made war upon his neighbors to exercise the people, which is what Plato had in mind, because idle citizens are insane men. Montezuma was grim of visage, and, as his appellation suggests, was a tyrant. No plebeian might look him in the face, and whenever a stranger defiled the air he occupied, his attendants fumigated him with incense.

Nations can expire of surfeit in fifty years. Montezuma was as much given to copal and the perfume of flowers as King Midas, who, after debauching his realm, offered Zeus his father's farm wagon.

Montezuma was as melancholy and as pusillanimous as Saul, and consulted witches every day long after he had heard of the arrival of Cortes whom he thought was the white-skinned *Quetzalcoatl*, god of *Cholula*. When his messengers returned from the camp of the Spaniards with a rich cloth on which were painted the ships and men of Cortes, he sacrificed a number of Indians and sprinkled their blood on these ambassadors, which was done when good tidings were received. Men endeavor to change their fate, for whether it is good or bad, they find it insupportable. Heliogabalus had the same need to swindle destiny and his assassins; he thought he could rob them of their joy, and that he would die as he wished. He sweetened his pond with roses so that, should they drown him in it, he would expire perfumed. He prepared a halter of twisted silk were he to hang; should he be stabbed he made ready a bodkin of gold, or could he avoid them altogether, he secreted poison in a box made of the unicorn. He died standing up to his chin in a privy, showing only his head, which was sufficient for his murderers.

Some say Montezuma was killed by a stone thrown by one of his vassals; others claimed that Cortes slew him; whatever his end was, his servant took his ashes and buried them in a contemptible place.

The Aztecs were as sensual as flowers; each of the eighteen months of the Mexican zodiac was a sign for maize, squash, sun and gore. The days were governed by the tiger, ape, and rain. Like the Tibetans, the Aztecs had five suns or catastrophes which destroyed the human race. One of these cycles began on the day four tiger, for those who did not perish by famine were eaten by tigers. They were the most cultivated cannibals in the world; the Indian hedonist slew people as though they were dahlias and poured forth their blood as if they were drawing out the odor of mountain clover. Had they

but eaten their gods instead of men, they would have been Gymnosophists or Pythagoreans, or one of the great symbolic peoples of the earth. Copal, the plumeria, their carnal flower, mountain tigridia, suffocated the Mexican to death.

They had Levitical wizards in their temples, the stones of which were hewn into snakes and snails; they cast incense on *Vitzliputzli* at daybreak, at noon, at sunset and at midnight, after which they beat themselves or drew blood from their legs with an obsidian dagger. There were the virginal boys, like the Inca vestals, who cleansed the floors and altars with the temple besom. These acolytes gathered scorpions, palmer worms, and spiders, of which they made an ointment for their gods.

Some of the priests who hated the human pudenda cast them away, but after that they flayed as many hapless slaves as before. Seneca writes of a man who constuprated a pair of wenches in a night, and since men are far more lewd than logical, we scorn the Aztec spado, and marvel at this deed of rapine.

The Mexican man-eaters were vegetable symbolists; their capes were made of the maguey root, and with the thorns of this plant the penitents pierced their sinning tongues. Like Empedokles, who made sacrificial kine out of myrrh and frankincense, the Aztecs wrought their deities out of corn paste, amaranth seeds, and beans. Venus was sea scum and *Vitzliputzli* was an image made of the paste of seeds, maize and honey.

War was the religious amusement of the Mexicans, and whenever they were in battle they rested every fourth day, which is the same custom the ancient Jews practiced as they would not fight against the Romans who besieged Jerusalem on their Sabbath. The Aztecs engaged in hostilities with nations to acquire captives for their oratories and their table. Water was their dwelling place, and blood nourished their lake lilies and rites.

Aztec art so admired as primitive was sanguinary. No forest or *Rio Negro* alligator or jaguar was the peer of the Aztec priest who cast incense to the four winds attired in the skin of a human victim.

The Aztec worked with the feathers of the parakeet; he was a lapidary in turquoise, an artisan in metals. His art was conceived in the head of the puma, the jaguar, the coyote, whose bones were interred with the remains of a mother or father. Art is a *huaca* with the belly of Moloch.

The Aztecs had numerous *Tlalocs*, or rain, thunder, and weather deities; *Tecutli* governed the four cardinal points, and gave the matmakers the fat reeds they needed. They made vows to their mountains, and moulded images in the shape of men to represent *Popocatepetl*, *Iztac Tepetl*, and the summits of *Poiauhtecatl*. The Inca took faggots and clothed them as people to be slain; they also flung into the coals of the brazier tallow, maize, opulent raiment, and children. In the month of *Atl Caualo* the Mexicans killed many children on the mountain peaks; this was the time when new fires were prepared, and the food for the Aztec Moloch was carried to its hapless end in a litter, followed by singing and dancing throngs, strewing flowers as they went.

The feast days of the Mexicans were Sabbaths in Tartarus. They had an idol of repentance, *Tezcallipuca*, who pardoned them every four years for their sins, and a god, *Tlaloc*, who gave them rain. The penitent trembled before *Tezcallipuca* who wore a jewel that covered his rank belly, and a greenstone at his navel. He was the Baal of the Mexican Golgotha, wrought of the heads of dead men.

Man-eating is the custom of all peoples, and it is better to sacrifice men to an Aztec idol with eyes of squash and teeth of beans for symbols than to do it as a liar, a hypocrite and for greed. It is not good for the man or woman offered to the gods to appease the blood, but it is better for humanity.

The annuity that the king paid to Cristóbal Colon for discovering a route to Cathay came from the taxes imposed upon the butchershops of Seville. This is a doleful reminder that the Christian is as much of a carnivore as any Indian flesh-eater.

The Inca and Aztec took the same pious care with the human flesh they offered to the idols as the Jews did with a ram or sheep brought to the altars of Elohim. The young victim was without a blemish; his teeth were as white as the sea conch; were his fingers stupid or obese, or if his navel hung, he was given brine to drink that he might become lean. At the feast of *Toxcatl* the victim went through the village sounding the flute and wearing jocund flowers; the palsied or lame children

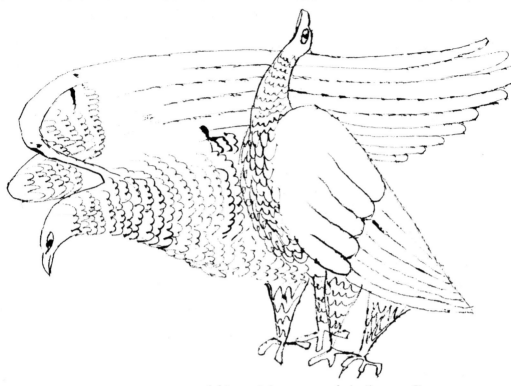

came to touch him and throw away their diseases. For twenty days he was Faustus, having four Indian Dianas, as virginal as woodland laurel, for his pleasure. Then, after the Aztec Faustus had come to the end of his days as a voluptuary, he broke his flute, and before he ascended the steps of the temple, *Tlacochalco*, the four Indian women wept and departed. When he reached the summit of the oratory, the priest plunged the obsidian knife into his breast, tore out the embered heart and raised it aloft to the sun.

During the feast of *Vitzliputzli* the priest came out of the temple in a surplice that fell as far as his hams, sounding an earthen fife which made every murderer, thief and adulterer shake. In Peru and Mexico adultery was punished by death, for no one wants to be taken for a cuckold, a title which would not create so much mockery were men not droll animals.

The mother of the gods was *Teeu Innan*, also called *Toci*; she was the spindle and broom deity, and the mummers at her feast wore nothing but a rope for a clout. The old men sang for her and beat a turtle-shell drum. *Tlacotteutl* was a divine woman who represented human perversity. This is a malign goddess who rules everybody. Paul relates in the *Epistle to*

the Romans that whatever he resolved to do, he seldom did. Most men, unable to endure their own lot, are ecstatic when others are galled; some attempt to bring harm to whole races of people by deriding their saints, or belittling Gethsemane or Moses on the rock, Choreb. It is alleged that one of the nails driven into the hands of Jesus was hammered into a horse's bridle for the emperor of Constantinople.

On some of their holidays, when *Ixcuiname* is celebrated, the Aztec starved his entrails. They held holy meals for *Chicome Coatl* who told them about quail-colored beans, the amaranth, and foods. They decked this idol in a shirt of the colors of a ripe lime, orange, or white maize blossoms. For the feast of *Tezcatlipoca* they chose a captive to be slain.

Work, penance, art and festivals were mingled. When there was drought, the priests of the *Tlalocs* fasted, abstained from women and offered copal to the gods so that the rains would come. During the rain festival, which took place in the sixteenth month, they made images of their mountains.

Uixtociuatl, adorned with squash blossoms, was their salt goddess. The people came from the marshes wearing wormwood flowers in their hair, and they sang and danced ten days for salt. At the end of their dances and orisons another became

79

the booty of the idols, slain with the snout of a swordfish.

In the ninth month of *Tlazochimaco* the people sought the mountain dahlia, the tigridia, the petals of the nymphæ, a Sierra ruffian magnolia, and the carnal plumeria. The young Aztec warriors wore long hair and were continent while the dotard Nestor and senile Menelaus drank wine, and great boasts wrinkled their toothless mouths and stomachs as they sat on the ground beneath the fires of *Popocatepetl*, remembering when they were volcanoes.

Chicomecoatl was the goddess of food and beverages, and *Centeotl* counseled physicians and midwives, and held a shield in one hand and a broom in the other. *Texacatlipoca* strode the heavens and earth and hell and sowed hatred and wars between men and nations. *Quetzalcoatl*, the deity of trade at *Cholula*, had a comb of warts, and stuck out his tongue. There were parturition, pest, abortion, plague and palsy idols. These deities give us clear knowledge of the people, whether they be despotic, stupid, grum, or vegetarian, and to what extent skulduggery and falsehood are venerated. There were trade gods; *Chalchiuhtily cue*, goddess of water, had power over seas and rivers, and her devotees were those who sold goods from their canoes, or those who vended fruits and herbs in big earthen jars in the market place. In Attica the market was a hallowed place; Socrates, Crates, and Zeno often went to the Agora where frankincense, poppy seeds, and mules were sold, and where the bones of Hesiod the poet were buried.

The Nahuas also had a goddess *Ciuacoatl*, a harpy Hecate who gave men misery and toil, the hoe and the tump–line, which are the thorns and the thistles into which Adam was cast. *Ciuacoatl* is a wise work figure, for men must toil, or die of satiety.

These remnants of Tartary knew the old Asian sins of Ham, and they set aside hermaphrodites which are like the apples of the Dead Sea whose core contained the clinkers of Sodom. The Pueblo Indians observed similar rites, and the Zuñis had androgynous deities. Indian women of Paraguay wore an image of the pudendum as an amulet. Stone and terra cotta effigies of Priapus were found in ancient graves in Peru and at Tabasco. Ancient phallic pillars stood in the Valley of Mexico, but they were the dead ruins of the *Tolteca* who came before the fierce *Chichimecas*. When the soldiers of Cortes came to *Panuco* they saw the Phallus in bas-relief on the walls of old temples. Men build edifices to Priapus which is no better than offering incense or a barren ewe to a disease. Such phallic stone obelisks are still to be seen in the lower Mississippi Valley and in Tabasco. Some of the Indian rites and customs of Eros who guards pulse and corn are saner testimonials of man's unquenchable sottishness.

The Indian was a cunning mime. The warriors of *Tlatelulco*, desiring to overcome the Mexicans, hid in the reeds, and simulated the shapes and noises of ravens, geese, and frogs. The Fuegians, who have no alphabet, can reproduce the gait of one of their tribe with more skill than Homer was able to limn Agamemnon or Nestor.

The Nahuatl words are of volcanic origin, and the consonants as rough as the peaks of *Tlaloc*, and rarely voweled. The Songs of Solomon to the Shulamite are soft water vowels, and the vanity therof is the cry of the turtledoves.

The materials of the Indian manuscripts show remarkable culture; the Aztecan papyrus was of the fabric of the *Agave* whose *maguey* leaves were employed as thatch for the roofs of the houses and as food and drink. The ancient Mexican also made rush seats out of the same reed with which he wrote.

The numeral seven was as holy to the Aztec as it is in the *Kabala*; could they have borrowed their marriage ceremony from the Chassidic sect? The Indian bride, like a mystic daughter of Israel, circled the groom seven times, her veil tied to his tunic.

Privy members of the Aztec children were cut, a practice similar to Jewish circumcision. The poor Indian brought quails to the demigods; in ancient Judea humble people brought a pair of turtledoves to the altar. Without a regard for penury man is a vile Plutus.

Penance was commonly observed, and though Sahagun tells us that only the old men and women confessed their vices, this shows unusual discernment; for the young there are the rigors and the sins, but for the aged there is confession and the waiting for death.

Except on the rarest occasions, only the old men and women, those who were heavy with desolation, and required wine or pulque to make them merry, were permitted to drink.

This merciful license is allowed the aged as is shown in *Proverbs*.

It is possible that what all men learn was known of old, and this is a miserable thought as each one would like to assume that he is better or knows more than Cain or Lamech or Manco Capac. The theogony of Hesiod is puerile to them who are certain they are not. But nobody is wise all the time, and only man, himself, could make such a boastful remark.

CHAPTER IX

The Inca was a Theban of the Andes; the first Inca came out of a crag at *Paucartampu*. The peaks of mountains were his *huacas* or idols; he venerated the Sierras and the Punas and his grief was dry. Rocks are the herbals of sun races. Medusa is less of a marvel than the hot fountain in the *Guancauilca* in Peru, which, as it pours forth, turns into pebbles. Stones are the remedies for the grieving mind and the flesh which are water and grass. Grass and rivers are the pleasures of men which pass away, but the ravines and hills mineral the will. The Egyptian embalmers at Heliopolis turned the head of the deceased away from the River Nile. The *Chotas* of Mexico worship the dawn and stones; *Tohil*, the god who gave the *Quiché Maya* fire by shaking his sandals, was of obsidian origin. The primal gods sprang up from an aerolite that had fallen from the skies.

The great cities were built on the verteber of the *Cordilleras*; the Andes travel to Chile, and on the route to that country are the mountains of *Pariacaca* where the air congeals the veins and makes sorrow flow like granite. These mountains have the same effect upon the mind as the climate of Quito where the Indians fell into a metaphysical melancholia and slew themselves; the pure air of Quito is the fire of philosophy, and will breed gymnosophists. The swans, by which the ancients meant priests and prophets, will appear in this land; men delight in such purity for it is best to die by philosophy; in the cave of Apollo there is a pool whose waters make men prophetic, though it shortens their lives.

On the days of the Inca's festivals the *huacas* were removed from the temples, and the mummies who had been lords and queens, were washed in the baths which they had used, and then carried in litters to the holy city of Cuzco. Here they gave *chichá*, boiled maize, to the embalmed ones. They also offered coneys, tallow, coca and raiment to the *huacas*.

When the demons were brought out for adoration the Inca abstained from salt; maids were chosen to carry the *chichá* in golden vases to the House of the Sun and the Thunder. During one of the festivals of the *Quiché Maya* a priest was sent to the woods to garner dew from leaves which had never been touched by woman.

The Inca banished the deformed from holy places save on certain feasts; the blind, the one-handed could not enter the temple of Jerusalem. A dwarf excites the perverse lusts; and a gnome from Punt was of more value to a Pharaoh than balsam or gold from Nubia. The sacrificial animal of the Inca and the Israelite was without defect; the Essene went in a white stole, and the Inca damsel wore golden shoes made of the fibers of the aloe tree.

Counting was held to be base by the Inca, and arithmetic, unless it is related to the pulsations of the sea, the moon, the setting of the Pleiads, or the harvest, is another word for avarice. They had unusual esteem for sages, or philosophers whom they called *Amatuas*, though the Inca had no alphabet. Letters is more of a fox than the tongue. The Aztec codices were the serpents we call art.

One who told falsehoods was punished by death; the slothful were mocked, and he who fell behind in his duties to the *huacas* had to carry toads fashioned out of salt. Those who kept their vows, and cast the ashes of Indian sheep, or the *guanacos*, and the sacred cloth into the river were allowed to bear lances and falcons wrought of salt. Inca morals are but the stems and boughs of Inca rituals. It is asserted that a female *huaca* having fornicated with a man was turned into a stone.

Great people seldom trust themselves, there is so little of man, either his arm, his hand, or his foot that arouses confidence. Either the elbow is craven, the fingers are ten perjurers, or the foot awakens licentious thoughts. When Amen-Rā, the sun-god, prevailed among the Egyptians, Pharaoh put the figure of Truth around his neck before judging the malefactor, nor could he say what penalty any fault was worth until the priests of Heliopolis consulted the papyri upon which the laws were written.

The first ancestor of the Inca is Manco Capac, child of the Sun, born of a rock which is more constant than the human heart. Manco Capac had three brothers of a more unstable nature, one called Ayar Cachi, signifying salt, the second, Ayai Vchu, a pepper, and the third Ayan Sanca, who is mirth and contentment.

Human appetite grows like the craw of Tantalus; once fed with salt or pepper for which the sensual nations sought a new route to *Cipango*, it ranges the world for more seasoned deliriums and voluptuous traumas. When man starves his gullet, he is entitled to the appellation Cato instead of his usual surname, cormorant.

Manco Capac founded the sacred city of Cuzco, and the maize and pulse raised there were priestly plants; an Inca seeing a pilgrim from Cuzco lowered his eyes or retired to one of his chambers.

Manco Capac taught the Inca to sow maize, for husbandry tames the passions. The Inca regarded savage or fallow ground as having a hardened heart. He instructed the Inca parents to press the heads of their infants until they were flat and stupid, for he thought that otherwise they would have round, virile craniums, and be insolent. The fathers of unruly children were severely punished. Youths at seventeen were given white breeches as a sign of their virtue and warrior strength. They retired to the hills, near Cuzco, to fast, and their fathers flogged them to remind them of their oaths and the valor of their ancestors.

He established houses for virgins who baked bread and wove the robes for the Sun; but no vestal or woman was permitted to enter the temple of the Sun. Manco Capac told the Inca that when girls combed and plaited their hair they were women. Not all work was equal. Some virgins were chosen to be porters; Yupanqui, a descendant of Manco Capac, ordered deformed and idiotic persons to be trained as weavers.

Manco Capac set the falcon, the hummingbird, snake, fox and toad in the hills. The boldest warrior is a falcon, the cunning one is a fox and a serpent, and the sluggard is a toad. Whatever the Inca learned from the falcon and the hummingbird was of small value, for the vices of the serpent, the fox, and the toad are much dearer to him.

Manco Capac told them of *Pachacamac*. Pacha is the Universe, and Camac is the Quickener. This name was as sacred as *Elohim*, and was not to be uttered by a pious Inca except when meditating or preparing to die. Until Manco Capac was old he was a philosopher. But when he was senile, he endeavored to find out who *Pachacamac* is, which is beyond the understanding of men. He prayed to the imageless Person, offering up an immaculate Indian lamb, hoping for some sign or word. The oval plate in the temple representing *Pachacamac* is an absolute blank. Unable to exact an answer from the Universe, he slew his son as a sacrificial gift, and so he became the Cain of the Incas.

Were it not that man is irrational either in the beginning or at the close of his life, Manco Capac would have been a god. His good principles confound men, his bad ones startle the puma.

A wise man may write a marvelous tragedy, and bray no less than the asinine penguin. In many ways he is less than Leviathan or Behemoth. Man is the most unstable brute, and knows less about himself than the widgeon, the fox or the seal.

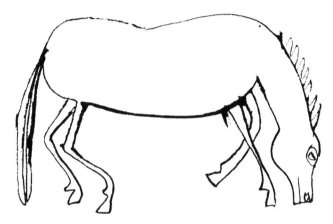

CHAPTER X

Francisco Hernandes de Cordoba and his men arrived at the Bay of Campeche, where they went ashore on Lazarus Sunday. Twenty Spaniards were killed, fifty wounded and those taken by the Mayans were sacrificed to their idols. With thirty-three holes in his body Cordoba returned to Cuba. What he told of the realm of Yucatan inflamed Hernando Cortes who left Cuba with a fleet of ships and men, his own pinnace bearing a banner honoring Our Lady.

Those who came to America seeking a new water route to Cathay found the remnant sons of Ham. All races are a confusion of first peoples, of Lamech, Japhet, Ham and Cush; the gross Cyclopes are said to be the progeny of Cush, the Egyptian pyramid builders, and his descendants, the Toltecs, architects of the temples at Cholula.

The races in the Plains of Shinar, in the Valley of Mesopotamia, and in Hellas have common origins; Greece was populated by the sons of Javan, and the Lacedaemonians acknowledge that they were of the same family as the Caphtorim of Palestine; genealogy is a vast myth; the record of man, apart from legend, is stepmother history.

The Tartarian Chan was Ham who was given Asia as his portion. The children of Ham wept for their forefathers; they had forgotten the wain and the wheel; and the elephant, the unicorn, and the horse had long since disappeared; instead of the buffalo that grazed in the pastures of Cathay, the North American Indian hunted, but did not yoke the bison. The bison is the woolly Indian buffalo, his cattle were deer, the hare and mute dogs. There were cow and wool trees in the New World, but no heifer or sheep, and no Joseph to dream of lean or fat kine.

The *Quiché Maya* had a jaguar *Genesis*, and they had an old Semitic word, Balam, meaning soothsayer; like the profane Balaam, in the *Old Testament*, this Balam was the jaguar priest.

Quiché is forest, for they were a tree people, longing to roof and bed their wives; and the title of their sacred book, made of tree bark, is *Popol Vuh*, which are *Quiché* words for together, or common house. Their knowledge of the first days of the earth came from the coyote, the owl and vampire bat; the ant told *Quetzalcoatl* where to find the corn seeds.

The *Quiché Maya* say that primeval man was shaped out of mud; Adam in Hebrew is virgin red clay. There are North American Indians who suppose that when the world was a circle of water, a crawfish brought up mud from the sea bottom. The Adam of the *Quiché* was unable to move his head, and his face fell to one side, and he could not look behind, which is the tragedy of the inhabitants of the New World. He had no mind, which is nothing else but turning one's eyes toward the past. These creatures were destroyed and were followed by figures of wood that peopled the earth; they were dry of cheek, and their feet and hands were stupid, and they had four parched legs. The women were fashioned out of river rushes, but nobody thought, and the men and women were wood, osier, and soulless legs and hands. They were drowned in the Deluge, or were devoured by eagles, or sparrowhawks, their nerves broken by bats, and their bones hewn to pieces by jaguars. Owls were their enemies, and so was pride which they called *Hunahpu*, the arrogant *Quiché* Nimrod, and the same *Quiché* word stands for fragrant flower.

Zipacna took their mountains to the sea where there were crabs to eat, and *Cabracan* was their earthquake giant. The Mayan, or his brother, the *Yaqui*, or Mexican, were flower priests who flensed human skulls; fennel, sage, and the odors of the delicate *tixzula* did not cure their murdering blood. A soldier of Cortes said that he counted a hundred thousand skulls on the racks in the Mayan temples.

The calendar of the Mayans and Aztecs was more accurate than the Julian year; the Inca set up weather towers on summits, and the Mayans erected square pillars, or sacred *Katuns* every twenty years. On these *Katuns* they kept many of the memorials of their forefathers; the Colchians had pillars on which they represented the continents of the world and Ocean. One of the earliest symbols for Zeus was a pyramid, the shape of fire. Prometheus, who is fire, was a castaway on Mount Caucasus hard by Colchis.

The Aztec and the Mayan had much reverence for the day and the month; every day is an Angel bringing men fortune or hardship, either of which requires the most austere discipline to endure. The *Quiché Maya* month of *Queb* is a deer and also the ear of green corn; *Tzizil Lakam* is the eleventh month when the sprouts show themselves, and desire pulls up the blood, and the maiden's petticoats. *Tziquin Kib* gathers the birds and their song, and *Cakam* is the time for red clouds· *Huahpu* is hunger, the wise Buddha of the covetous stomach.

There were eighteen months in the Mayan year, and a devil for each who received copal or bread and calabash seeds. They showed their adoration for the month, *Muluc*, by bringing to its image fifty-three grains of ground maize and copal. In the month they called *Mol*, the artisans gathered cedar out of which they carved the deities. At this time they fasted and had no commerce with women. There was a month called *Nabey Man*, signifying the first old man or evil omen, for where there is no strength there is no hope of good chance or a wise fate, for neither Zeus nor Aphrodite, nor Pallas Athene pay any heed to the weak.

Three months are given to white flowers; they hold that there are five barren days, which are very few, had they not dropsical demons, or did they not cringe before *Tatan bak* and *Tatan Holom*, one the father of bones, and the other of skulls. They have a strong awe of death and rot; their word, *Cayala*, means the yellow ears of corn, which is their principal food, but *Cay* is the putrid matter in water from which maize first sprang.

The names they give their days are not the Indian crater words, but are China or Tibetan travelers; *Tob* is rain or tempest, and *Imox* is fish, *Cat* is a weir for a lizard, or an iguana whose meat they relish. There was the cacique *Nachen Can*; *Can*, like *Atl*, or *Ch'en*, Indian months, are Tartary words. The *Quiché Maya* months have the same Asian origin, and this is old world understanding. They brought their month and day names from the China mainland, carrying them in their heads, as they did their gods, or *Bacabs*, upon their backs.

Many of the idols of the Mayans are naked figures of men whose genitals are covered by long fillets. Though these Indians regarded human flesh as the most palatable venison they hated thieves; their houses had no doors, which is very wise, since men usually take what is hidden from them. It was very costly to filch a Mayan maidenhead, for they seized the malefactor and drew out his intestines through the navel. For the seduction of another's wife, they stoned the adulterer to death. They elected the most beautiful women to pour water or wine from the calabash, which they did turning away from the men as they served them.

The *Quiché Maya* have a barbaric Virgin Mary, *Xquic*, Little Blood, whose father is *Cuchumaquic*, the Blood-Gatherer. Their hero is *Hhun-Hunahpu* who is a skull in the Calabash tree. Whoever partook of the fruit of this heathen Tree of Life ate a human head. *Xquic* had a great pining to have one of these gourds, and reaching for the fruit a few drops of tree spittle fell from the fruited skull upon her and she conceived. She is the mother of the Aztec god of war, *Huitzilopochtli*.

At *Chiapas* there is the dragon tree which bleeds; the tree of Cochineal sheds those tears of gore which satisfy men no less than Patagonian ore. The tree is an Indian god, and each locality is his kindred. He is not alone in the forests, among the rocks, or in the thistles, and the Mayan knew little of that fever cankering all men, being apart. Suffering together is the lesser pang, and the Mexican and the Mayan tell how the

tribes, after they had left Panuco, wandered in the woods together, having lost the sacred seeds *Quetzalcoatl* gave them.

The natives of Yucatan were as vulnerable to odors as the vine which is queasy when it is near the cabbage or the radish. Whether people smell good or not is the reason for considering them virtuous though Lazarus and Doctor Samuel Johnson stank. Chastity, too, is what the nose thinks is savory; the Indians honored the virgin-cloth, but did not think a widow worth a wedding. When an Indian desired to marry a widow, he went to her house, and if she gave him food they were man and wife. The Mayan traveler took with him incense and a small brazier in which to burn it, and he paid homage to the *Bacabs* of the Four Directions by perfuming the stones which stood for them.

They filled the mouth of the dead with maize, and after sawing the hinder part of the cranium stuffed it with some kind of mumia, or bitumen, as the ancient Egyptians did. They abhorred theft, homicide, and liars; as they used cacao for money and stones for counters, and many held their lands in common, there was little cause to steal. The European lied to increase his fate; the Indian only told falsehoods to protect his earth.

The Indian mother had the copious paps of the Ephesian Diana, because she ground maize without tying up her breasts, and she often gave her milk to a deer or a dog. Indian women baked the cassava bread or washed their clothes in the rivers with a soap made of the ashes of the elm, but there are few chronicles of their amorous inclinations. In North America the Indian woman rises from her sleep, when the moon has risen, and dances naked around the maize she has sown. Among the natives of Brazil a man spoke to a woman with his back turned towards her, which is often more sensible than facing her which he cannot do without showing her his genital organs. The Indian woman, wearing a cloth that dropped no farther than her navel, is said to have been as modest.

The Caciques at *Tlaxcala* sent Cortes gold and silver, feathers, raiment, soles for sandals, and four Indian crones, which greatly displeased his soldiers. A fat *curaca* presented his ugly niece to Cortes, and as he knew how to smile as well as Iago, he put on a joyful face. Pedro de Alvarado, who ravished Yucatan and Guatemala for Hernando Cortes, hung one Indian damsel and a wife on a tree because he said their beauty would make the Spaniards discontented. When the *Quiché Maya* declared war upon Alvarado they crucified a virgin puppy and a woman in a ravine.

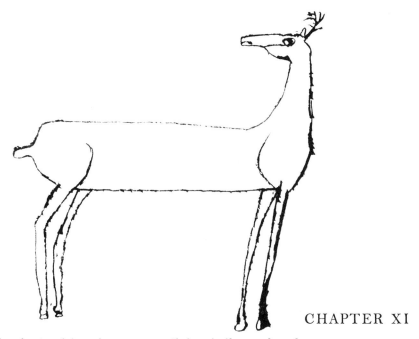

CHAPTER XI

The hot lands of America grow prodigies similar to the tale of the *Camucuiara* who are said to have paps that nuzzle their knees, and which they bind around their waists when they run or hunt. The stories about unipeds, people with horse's feet, and dog's heads, are Hesiodic fable and zoology. Magellan saw Patagonians who were eight feet tall, though Darwin assures us they were no more than six.

Brazil is a Canaan in the morning, but a scorpion and a spider by midday. One voyager has observed the climate flows with poison. There is scarce a stone from the sea coast by *Pernambuco* to the Province of the Holy Ghost, and men are impatient and gross infidels without rocks or Sierras. Energy is a mighty god, and the Indian word for the great, brute waters is *Parana*; there is the bursting flood, the *Paranambuco*. But the rivers of Brazil are angels sown with dragon's teeth.

The most infamous eaters of human flesh are the humid water nations of the Americas. They dwell in the *Sertãos* of Brazil or people the gloomy lake regions. They are fierce hunters greedy for incense and flowers; the falcon is a bird of rapine whose breakfast is the hummingbird which dotes on the honey of flowers. Their animals are hot and loathly, either giving off the evil odor of the fox, or the fragrance of the musk snake. Their food is a galling fillip to the stomach and the soul; Indian pepper is called *Carib*, a cannibal spice which kindles lusts; they eat battle bread made from the savage, spinous yucca; the *mandioca* root provides them with another kind of bread, although the juice is fatal.

The face of these natives is homogeneous, lacking the havoc and the rueful lines which are the work of the intellect. The nose, though Caucasian, which has the long, aquiline look of a Euripides or a Solon, is a mummer of thought. The Indian seldom balds, and many men would become savages solely to be as hairy as the bear or the pard.

These natives are raw patriarchs; the Indian Abraham cuts the navel string with his teeth, which gives him the right to rule his children. There is no patricide by the River of January, for when a child is peevish or unpleasant, the father lashes him; they have enough tenderness for their children to protect them from growing up to be gourmets or indolent. The Inca despise gluttony, giving the infant the breast to suck three times a day, no matter how much he cries for more of his mother's teats. The natives of Brazil beat their children with thistles to harden them sufficiently to dwell in the woods. Some of the aboriginals never chastise their children, who, after they have reached puberty, are as irascible as the fly.

The Brazil native governs his wife, seldom quarreling with her, and when he hates her he waits until he is drunk to strike her so that he can blame the wine for his act. He shows a marvelous regard for women, permitting only withered crones or virgins to prepare his wine; the maids and hags take the *mandioca* root into their mouths, and after champing it between their teeth spew the juice into a calabash.

There are as many tribes in Brazil as there are rivers, and their names have been catalogued as the descendants of Cush, Ham and Japhet are, and they eat men. A brave Indian of

Brazil, about to be devoured by his captors, said it was better to be the venison of man than to die and stink and be a meal for worms. There are seventy-six nations of the *Tapuyas* who are anthropophagous; their enemies are the *Tapuxerig* who call themselves their foes so that they can devour their corn fields without feeling unjust.

Most of the Indians in these regions were cannibals; the tribes, as well as the waters of this land, are tributaries of one another as Put and Canaan are the sons of Ham. The natives living between the upper *Orinoco, Rio Negro,* the *Inirida,* and the *Jupura* devoured human flesh. For the lack of cattle they ate men; there was no pastoral life, and the natives of the *Orinoco* traveled with the seeds of corn, squash, beans, melons. In the place of poultry the timorous inhabitants of the Indies who brought calabashes, plantains, cassavas, and tears to Cristóbal Colon, fed upon the macaw whose skin is black and tough. Bears that frequented the shores of the *Temi* were considered savory table meat by the Indian. The *Guahibos* fed on scolopendras and worms rather than sow cassava or maize. The horse in America became a nomad on the *llanos* and would have been a cannibal Indian or one of the steeds of Diomedes who were said to care for human flesh.

The *Tapoyes* inhabit the coast, and their name in the Indian language means a wild man, a word held in exceptional derision among the cannibals of Brazil. The *Waytaquazes* at *Cape Frio* are very fierce and can take a huge dogfish by the tail and haul it ashore. The *Wayannases* have their habitation south of the River of January; they are notorious poltroons, and their daintiest victual is man. The *Petivares* are not so barbaric; they make a hole in their lips with the horn of a roebuck; they are naked and range northern Brazil from *Baya* to the *Rio Grande,* and they eat everybody.

Cannibalism was the sin of the Anakim, the giants who were the progenitors of Cyclops. This unnatural gluttony was practiced by the Laestrygones who worshipped snakes. The American savage consumed people as well as toads, serpents, crocodiles, and they named their great waters after them. The Sirens beckoned the mariners to the coasts of Italy where they were shipwrecked and became the meal of the Lamii.

After passing the River of *Paraeyva,* one comes to the country of the *Molopaques,* who cover their secret parts, and

have much gold which they do not care for and use on their fishing lines in the River of *Para*. Their women are very modest, and never laugh; wit, the parent of malice and of letters, is not one of the traits of primitive nations. The *Motayas* come dancing and singing to meet strangers, bringing them the *mandioca* root and pepper as gifts. They abhor the *Tamoyes* and devour them whenever possible. The women are exceedingly hospitable, and as soon as a guest arrives, they weep bitterly over him and caress his shoulders and knees, a custom that arouses very envious feelings in occidental nations.

These savages have a houseless hardihood; the *Guaitica* do not inhabit their huts except when they go to bed. The Indians of the *Orinoco* and of the *Atures*, abounding in granite, pay little heed to doors, and have no keys of which creeds and rosaries are made; the *Piaroas* that live near the little *Catanaiapo* wear the teeth of the peccary around their necks. Some of the tribes do not sup on human flesh; the *Cumpache* are content to cut off the heads of people who trouble them. The *Carayas*, who occupy the banks of the Upper Saint Antonio, kill defenseless foreigners, but barter courteously with those who have weapons. The climate produces too many rivers; the heat engenders the dwarfish *Tarape*, and those who call themselves the *Nonea* and who have immense faces which can do little else but gawk. The *Tupinaquin* are a revengeful brood; they lie with all women, or as many as they have the strength for, and are now reported to be Christians. Cannibals are not interested in rapine or the occidental disease called love, and do not find it essential to practice furtive polygamy, as a woman can be had for a knife or a hatchet.

Sancta Cruz is the Christian appellation of this country whose rivers and bays bear the names of apostles and Saint Francis, the sainted pauper. Brazil is a red wood and a tree of trade; cacao grains were Indian money; in Guiana the inhabitants used small snails for currency. Greed diminishes the virgin energies, and man is as weak as grass. Metals also sorrow; Galen and Monardes write that iron suffers a grievous disease which can be cured by anointing it with the marrow of a deer.

The trees of Brazil know more than Aesculapius or Hippocrates; the bark of the *Acaiu* tree is a remedy for sores and imposthumes. This tree distills a gum that is good to paint with; worms provided the Mayans with some of their pigments which artists use as though they were drunkards. It was long ago remarked, and, alas, since forgot, that painting is a book for fools who cannot read.

The *Ombu* is a water trunk more precious to travelers than pride; the *Cabueriba* is esteemed for that balm wearied Jeremiah sought in Gilead; wounded animals rub themselves on this bark until the liquor pours forth upon their hurts. The *Igcigca* gives the sweet-smelling mastic which takes the place of incense. There is a species of Brazil peach good for the pox; the flower of the *Caaroba* is reported to be as fine a medicine as China Wood for those who are mocked by Venus. In the land of the macaw Adam's tree is known as the *Pacoba*, the leaves of which cool grief and the ague. The *Moriche* palm is a water tree, growing about the *Guayaval* and the *Piritu*; this is the tree of raiment, and wine and flour of the *Guaraunos* who say the serpents give them moisture which the forests require. The palm tree of the Pampas could not afford enough shade for a melancholy Saul or a parched Jonah. The milk of the pawpaw is nutritious, but it does not take the place of the heifers of the Amaleks or the paps of Diana. The *Tamanac* believe that after the flood South America was repeopled by the seeds of the *Mauritia* palm tree from which they sprang. The priests at Hermopolis had the branches of palms in their sandals and were as wise as the Chaldeans. In Yucatan the giant *Ceiba* is regarded as the Tree of Life, but no one has ever eaten of this wood.

The cocoa tree is the olive of South America, but it thrives upon salt water which kills men or drives them mad. Beyond the cataracts of *Ature* and *Maypure* are cocoa groves, but these regions are plagued with worms, ants, insects, and cannot assuage the weariness of the Psalmist. Trees are wanderers too, and they suffer from the worm, the wart, and acquire novel or deranged habits in strange climes; the *mamee-apple*, the plantain, and the alligator pear thrive upon sea water, and can be said to be original but perverse flora.

Wild trees are the hardiest, but they produce no fruit; the palms of the *Mauritias* of South America, furnished the Indian with threads for hammocks and beverages rather than legends; Euripides writes that Latona gave birth to Apollo and Diana beneath a palm tree, and Homer tells us that Phoenix, one of the horses of Diomedes, was the color of a palm.

CHAPTER XII

The hot lands of America are a snake fable. When Cortes arrived on the shore of *Chalchicuecan* in 1519, there was not one domestic animal in *Terra Firma*; the elephants had long since vanished, and only extinct fossils of the horse have been found.

There was no shepherd, no Virgil or Propertius to lament the feral peccary, tapir, armadillo, condor, or guanaco. Jacques Cartier had called the New World *Terra damnata.*

Man is the most vain of all the animals in the earth, though in most respects he is no better than a polypus, which also has a mouth, intestines, and organs. Man is more superstitious and his manners are more irregular than these creatures, and his malice is more essential to him. Aristotle has said that animals only die at neap tide, but men perish wantonly in all months and seasons.

Wild ground produces the worst feeders; putrid whale or seal blubber is a great delicacy for the Fuegian, whereas in the central part of *Tierra del Fuego* hummingbirds drink the pith of flowers, and parrots rejoice in the seeds of Winter's Bark. The civet cat of Brazil is a remarkable teacher; its diet is honey, but none is touched until the young and the senile cat is called to join in the meal. The armadillo tastes like the flesh of the hen and has the muzzle of a sucking pig; wallets are made of the skin of this barbed horse, which were better for mankind were they sieves. The peccary is the hog of the woods; the tapir pastures only at night, abhorring the sun, and is as perverse a prodigy of the New World as the Indian.

The sloth bellies the ground as it goes, but it is as delicate a feeder as the ancient Essene, starving to death without fig leaves. The *jacuacini* are wallowing brutes, slubbered with sleep, who eat sea crabs and browse among the sugar canes. The *jagoarucu* are Brazilian dogs with the teeth of eagles who dote on fruit. The *tapati* are coneys who bark, and the *pacai* are feral pigs that swim in the Saint Francis. The *macucagua* is a very small bird; when it sings it is an omen of spring rains, but when it eats it shows the crop of Cerberus.

The lizard adorns the sterile lava isles in the Pacific, and this primal creature is herbivorous and without malice, for he is as content with sea weed as Diogenes was with a peck of lupines. The Galapagos tortoise, the finch and the lizard eat the cactus together as brothers.

The condor, a carrion feeder, is a social bird that lives in pairs, and in parts of South America these garbage-eaters roost together with others of their kind in trees. It is said of the *Polyborus Chimango* that when he is in a passion he plucks up the grass to satisfy his rage, but this is a feathered cenobite, and though men go into the wilderness to quell their spleen, few come out of the forest with a timorous mien or spirit. The ostrich in Northern Patagonia lives on roots and grass and prefers to be apart from others. When man is separated from companions he is a swinish eater, without domestic affections, dwelling meanly in deserts or caverns, and without fables to ease his bile or warm his bowels for others.

The *anima* is a rapacious bird, and the Indians say that the horn on its comb or beak is a remedy for people whose words fall out of their mouths too early or late. Other birds of prey are the falcon, merlin, eagle, and the goshawk. The fishermen of Galilee were no gentler than this predatory fowl until it had knowledge of men.

Nature riots in the hot lands of the New World, and surfeit begets monsters and griffins Homer dare not fable. A serpent has two mouths, one in its tail. Another has the skin of the prickly pear.

There is a great ape whose whiskers sprout in the lower chap, and wherever he goes he is accompanied by a wean. When this large, hairy Esau cries out, foam gathers on his beard which the young one wipes away. The monkeys that inhabit the woods and the banks of the *Apure* or the *Rio Negro* cleave to the parents as Ruth did to Naomi. They cling to the backs of their mothers which have been killed by arrows or darts, and must be torn from them. They fear very much to be hurt, and if they perceive any danger, their eyes fill with the waters of Heshbon.

Brazil, the land of the popinjays, christened *Sancta Cruz*, has the energy of the serpent. The Indian, when bitten by a venomous reptile, drank from the horn of the unicorn, known as snake wood. When an Indian woman is barren she is struck on the hips with a snake. On the holy days of the Aztecs the virgins wear vines of maize and the bones of vipers. Neither the fig nor the cocoa tree has subdued them. The poison of the *Jararaca* flows from a tooth like saffron water. The animals confound the senses as though the species of one had coupled with those of another.

Men are more bizarre than animals. They are as jealous as the male crocodiles in the coupling season. The guanaco, before domesticated by man, pays little heed to the female, but after he has lived in association with human beings, he bites any one who approaches the dam in his corral. The guanaco has ridiculous passions and a slavish noddle; he prances before his assassin, making silly, amorous capers; these beasts march in platoons to the salinas, for salt water refreshes their throats. But no ancient barrow or cenotaph is more noble than the dying guanaco, who crawls to the marge of a river to leave his bones by the waters. His end is more important than his life. We would be indifferent to human fate were it not that man dies.

Men take their habits from animals, and they lose their symbolic life apart from them. They are also as vehement as the reptiles in the earth they have not cured. Man is without calm until he has sown his follies in the matrix of Tamar, and he is as mournful afterwards as the swan who sings his own dirge. The mastic, the nutmegs, and cloves for which he had ploughed all seas are chaff in his head and his one cry is for a crypt, an epitaph, the funeral worms.

Man is the tragic animal and is as waspish as the *yapu* bird, who has a strong odor when he frets. He makes many books which are intolerable scorpions, which, in Brazil are said to sleep in men's boots, and to be ecstatic when lying in the libraries.

The legends of a continent without household animals, timorous streams, and social birds, except the macaw and parrot bred in the swamps of the *Sertão*, are battle Kabala of creation. It is told that after the Deluge the coyote planted the feathers of the various birds from which sprang up all the tribes of men.

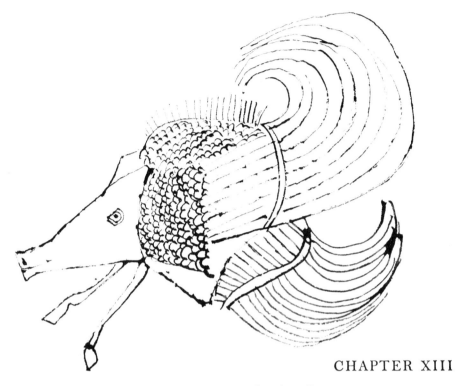

CHAPTER XIII

The four rivers of Paradise water all wisdom; the Pison flows about Havilah, near the mouth of the Indus; the Gihon is the Nile, the Tigris is an Assyrian arrow, and the Euphrates is called Perath in *Genesis*; their children are the Mississippi, tumulus of De Soto, and the five tribal inland seas of the Iroquois and the Hurons. There is the Colorado, the *Rio Palmas*, or the Rio Grande, the Missouri, and these are our heads, loins, and dorsal muscles, still Indian fetch, and to be canonized and resettled. The River of January is the body of Poseidon which covers more than fourteen leagues of the land of Brazil. The *Orinoco* and the *Meta* are the beds of the croco-dile, the eels or gymnotus; the *Rio Guarico* falls into the *Apure*, and beyond the *Meta* and the *Arauca* is *El Dorado*. These waters are no laughing nymphs, and Michael, the Archangel, who saw Adam by the Jordan, had not blessed the *Rio Negro* or the furies of the *Amazon*.

There are no apocalyptic waters in *Terra Firma*, and we know of no Daniel who stood on the banks of Ulai, or of a Baruch weeping over the captivity of Jerusalem upon the River Gel. The continent is still a massive valley of Jehosaphat, and whether it contains the bones of an Isaiah, or if the prophets be those mastodons which the moon melted when the children of Noah divided the earth, is unknown. The rivers of the New Hemisphere belong to the first six days of creation; the cosmographer quarries every stream and current; for water is the seer of dream, which was the map in the heads of Cartier, Cabot and Cabral.

America is battle earth and its rivers are great water brutes; the *Rio Negro*, the *Parana*, *Da Prata*, are unsocial waters, the navel strings of Ocean. Sea calves and whales swim in the bays and at the mouths of the rivers where the bivalves sing.

The River of Toads is hard by the River of Saint Francis, and there is another marvelous stream called Saint Michael. The Angel Uriel stands guard over Cocytus and Phlegethon in Tartarus, but it takes a long time for men to learn how to weep by the marges of rivers.

The guitar strings, made of the muscles of a boa or from the intestines of the *alouate* monkey, did not provide the songs of the swans that made Apollo melancholy. When rivers age, and grow small and mild, Daniel, Artemis and Pan frequent their banks. Water in its dotage is the cause of a psalm or a poem, for Neptune, Poseidon, and Proteus, who are water, are old men, and the swan's most poignant song is known as his senilia, and the River Strymon was his ancient home.

Our annals are weak, and we know not our rivers; we cannot understand today which is Father Rā, the Egyptian sun, until we gather up yesterday, who is Osiris. These rivers are immense legends and would cure us of many ills, did we know them, for all nature is our corpus, and once we relinquish a part of the earth, we lose, in some way, the use of our hands, feet, loins, and spirit.

The Florida current was a seer, as great a navigator as Cristóbal Colon or Magellan or Drake; the gulf, the warm channel in the Sea of Darkness, was an intimation of a passage to Japan; there had been hints of the existence of a world beyond the Pillars; the trunk of a *Cedrela odorata* was found at Santa Cruz near Teneriffe; two red-skinned corpses had been washed ashore at the Azores; the beaches of Gomera were strewn with fruits from the Antilles; storms had driven Esquimaux in canoes of wolves' skins, to the Orkneys. Nature divulges its secrets, but man is slow to fathom them. The tortoise, coming from the waters of Cuba, and found on the coasts of Scotland, was a quicker cosmographer than man.

Vulcan, known to the ancients as a navigator, had revealed none of his knowledge to the Indian who remained in the Americas; only the corpses, some bamboo trees from Brazil, cane, and the trunks of the *Ceiba*, journeyed to Europe, and none, except *Quetzalcoatl*, and his retinue, left the land of Dido or shipped out from Tyre, or Sidon, to thresh a sea for an American fate.

The River Achelous heaped up the mud for the Echinades islands, and Delos was a gift of the seas; Memphis was the bodies of Thetis and Neptune which are ancient sea water, but the *Orinoco*, the *Uruguay*, and the *Amazon* are as old as Deluge. The coffer of the *Orinoco* is wrought of granite. Stone and water shape the character of peoples. Rocks and rapids winter the blood and give a grum honesty to the tribes. The lecherous crocodile abhors the cataracts.

The *Orinoco* is the bed of the emu and the manatee, whose fat was burnt as oil in the lamps in the churches. The manatee is marine table pork for the Indians of Brazil; born in salt estuaries, the manatee goes to fresh water to drink and feeds on the leaves of the mangrove tree. This animal has the flavor of an ox, and its intestines are laden with grass. When there is a dearth of this mammiferous animal, or when he goes to other fresh-water seas, the *Ottomac* eats earth. The emu is a big river sheep. There is a fish called the caribe whose belly is a serrated saw, and can cut a crocodile to pieces, which is also the proper appellation of these rivers that would be the visage of God were they not voracious.

Four watery Nimrods flow over the back of the *Cordilleras*, and they are the *Meta*, the *Guaviare*, the *Caqueta*, and the *Putumayo*. Rivers make men contemplative and slake the soul. Large, feral waters confound the races of the earth. New ground is too original for men, and the animals are paradoxes. Wild man goes to the marshes where the crocodiles swarm.

The white heron treads upon the scaly back of the sleeping reptile; the saurians and the jaguars show diverse habits in various great streams.

Carved emeralds have been found in Quito, and some fix *El Dorado* on the declivities of the Andes; rivers of gold rise in this mountain. The mountains of *Encaramada* and the ranges of the *Mato* were the matrix of the *Rio Asiveru*. The fearsome turtle inhabits the beaches where the *Orinoco* and the *Apure* are twined together; the jaguar, the crocodile come here for meat and poultry which the tortoise provides. The natives gather on these banks during the turtle-rains, when the egg harvest is abundant, but the crocodiles and the tigers wait for the tortoise to lift its head above the surface of the waters. The turtle lays its eggs after sunset, and hides them in holes on neighboring islands, but the jaguar, the saurian, and the vulture pursue them.

The voice of the crocodile is heard during the turtle-rains, when she is calling to her young; when the savannahs are deluged the colt swimming toward the mare is the booty of this beast. The crocodiles of *Angosture* eat men, but in the *Rio Neveri* they do not trouble them; this reptile abhors the *Rio Negro*. Gnats, mosquitos, and the azury *zancudos* scorify human flesh at the *Rio Magdalena*. On the rocks along the banks of the *Cassiquiare* there are figures of the sun, the moon, tigers, and saurians, but these were never translated into Diana, or the Satyrs.

There are bastard seas which have a low and high tide, like the *Champoton* and the *Rio de Lagartos* in Yucatan. These are salty summer waters which make men lethargic, so that their sole concern is an adipose iguana, the sun, or weaving.

The immense *llanos* are still recent ocean bottom; the *Amazon* is known as a great fresh water sea, but Poseidon must search for Demeter for hundreds of years, because the burning plains are sterile, and the vast masses of polypi, the relics of a fleeing Atlantic, do not season vices, or perfect the soul.

The *Zama, Mataveni,* the *Atabapo,* the *Tutuamini,* the *Temi* are the waters of Ham, for they are black; the waters of Joppa are red, but this is Adam's flood; the *Cassiquiare,* which flows into the *Rio Negro,* is white; the two tributaries of the *Cassi-*

quiare are the *Siapa* and the *Pacimony*, but one is fair, the other dark; the *piritu* palm trees that fringe the black river of the *Atabapo* are thorny psalms; Linnaeus asserted that the country of palms was the original abode of man, and that man is by nature palmivorous; the Indians in this region live for months on the fruit of the *piritu* palm trees.

The Portugals canonized the rivers of Brazil, naming them after Raphael and Our Lady, but first waters are reptiles, then they are idols, and later harlots after whom the *Rio Magdalena* was called. The names of the Indian waters, the River of the Stones, of the Toads, and of the Crocodiles, are more learned hydrography.

The New Hemisphere is a great ruin, and its rivers are the holy sepulchres which are as noble as the graveyards of Eridu and Borsippa. The plains of Uruguay are the cemetery of the Megatherium, and the rivers of the western hemisphere are the archives of lost peoples. Savages often have more piercing burial-rituals than civilized nations. Certain Indians have a tradition that wherever they die, they are soon afterwards interred in the hollowed bark of a tree in the bank of a stream. The past of America is as unknown as that site in Mount Nebo where Moses is buried.

Nations are children everywhere, and the rituals in all countries are very much the same, for they are tributary rivers of one great parent stream, Ocean, the father of Earth.

History is honey in the head of Plato; it is told that no dew or rain fell upon the hills of Gilboa after Saul and Jonathan were slain there by the Philistines. Let us take up the pipes, harps, and Psaltries which Jubal gave us and sing our annals; this is Indian pagan land, let us claim it; it is our crib and our deity; our arms are miserable earth, and our hands a thousand sins, and we will be waifs and Ishmaels, utterly kinless, and we cannot come into our own Golgotha, or native agony, until we cry, Abba, Abba, for every river is the descendant of Abraham, Isaac and Jacob.

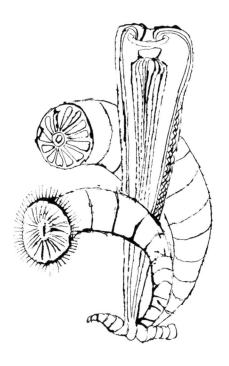

CHAPTER XIV

The Mississippi is the parent of the canes that fringe the banks; the walnut, the mulberry, the maple and oak are homage to the river. This Spirit waters the earth for thousands of leagues of man, and the Indians called this god Mechasipi. Some rabbin of yore or Syriac thinker claimed that the Spirit is three cubits long, but this is Kabbalistic speculation, as the head does not contain so much water, soul, or meditation. Hennepin called it the *Colbert,* and the priest Marquette, *Concepcion.* The stream *Akansa* comforts the aspens, mothers the beans and the medlars; the *Chickasaw* is the house-parent of the laurel, the elm and the mulberry tree. The five lakes are the elders of the continent, but the Fatal River is the Holy Ghost of America.

Rivers are uncured, nomadic waters until they are myths· The *Chicahominy,* the River *Powhatan,* discovered by Captain

John Smith, are Indian graves rather than the living vines of waters. When Egypt was first peopled it was a morass, and at the time John Smith arrived in the country of Virginia, there was no grass there except what grew in the marshes. The land and rivers of Louisiana were as bitter as Orcus.

La Salle called the Province he explored Louisiana, which was as vast as the territory of Shem which extended from Jerusalem to India. This region went as far South as the English Carolinas, and its western boundaries were the *Mechasipi*, the Missouris, and the *Obache* River.

Strabo, De Soto and La Salle were river geographers. Man cannot achieve knowledge except what water yields to mortal mind. Truths are in the bitter marshes of the deceased. La Salle had a February genius; he was a cold cosmographer, having fewer vices to moult than Cortes and De Soto. The Cavalier had little of earth, air, fire; he was as dour as the peninsula rock of Araya; mica slate feigns a sterile mien, and is water bottom, but the garnet trembles there. It is doubtful that he ever found the source of the *Mechasipi* which is warm and falls into the Gulf, because character, free will and destiny are the same. La Salle chose Canada, and North America, a Golgotha's Vineyard, as his water and burial site.

Seeking the Fatal River, the French saw tracks of wild goats in some sloughs. The lakes were covered with teal, water-hens, bustards. There were herds of plovers pecking ruined pools. They imagined they were near the Magdalen River. There were rattlesnakes among the brambles which the starved men ate when they could kill them. Alligators slept in the marshes; the musk of this reptile comes from its cod; the meat is white, and sweet, but few of the French had any stomach for it.

At Lake Huron the men dug up acorns under the snow, having no other food. They had planted melons, endive, parsnips, pompions, but the birds and animals ate the seeds. Herbs, vegetables and death came into the world on the third day. Besides the wild garlic in the marshes, and the small onions growing on the mesa, they had no other aliment or solace but the plant of death.

The wolves had left four feet of a deer which the French seethed in the *Pottowattamie* village. Decayed pumpkins, the

thongs and the shield of a bison were their rations until they reached *Missilmakinak*.

Brambles and willow were his portion out of which he fashioned withes to knot an otter or beaver. The severest deity is need, a god who confers benefits upon men who toil with chance.

There was no home-coming to Ithaca for La Salle. The waters of Styx flowed through his head. No Calypso detained him in a recondite Orphic cave; the violets, the purslane that sprang up in the bog had never been pacified by Ceres, and the prairie hemp was savage. Polybius says that Menelaus went to Joppa, founded by Japhet, but La Salle, a far greater navigator, discovered cannibal towns, some Indian remnants, the Miamis at the source of the *Teatiki*, the *Outagamia* on the banks of the Green Bay. He had not built one colony, or left any chronicles; murdered by his own men, the journals of his feats were kept by faithful, but sterile companions. Father Hennepin endeavored to steal his exploits, and to claim for himself the role of Ulysses or Jason, but no one can filch the character of another man, or harm his fame. Whoever Homer was there is no other.

Memory is our day of water tutored by want. La Salle sought virgin Tartars, descendants of Prometheus. He returned to Frontenac, but he had not found the Alpha of the River.

Water is death, but man must seek it. All our seeming wakings are the debris of evening waters; most dreams come from mean shallows, and are the digestive rot of secure bottoms; prophecies rise up from the marine depths ancient as the Flood. We are cartographers, unheeding the singing maggots, or bereft of the Angel.

CHAPTER XV

Primeval potherbs send their roots down far; the manna ash run deep into the earth. The Indian is a forest people; the deity of the *Tupi* tribes is called Caypor, a sylvan god who dwells in the woodlands where he hunts pacas and deer. The baboon of the Old World lives on the ground, but the apes of America are arboreal. The Stone Indian sits in the branches and chants to Keetche Manitou before the bison hunt.

This is wild land, undomestic; the natives have a legend of a shaggy tree-Esau, called Curupira, unmentioned in *Genesis*. The Para estuary is a wild water hymn. How long does it take savage ground to produce the damsels of Jerusalem, or Dido? Praise be Linnaeus for calling a butterfly Hetaera Esmeralda; man is the thrall of an amorous name.

Sow soft fruits in crabbed weather for etesian winds roughen the furrow of the olive. Broom flowers in dry places. Fir, hemlock and the yew are mountain wood, dour is their fruit; these are no treason's summer friends. Gall-oak, sea-bark, hilly ash and poplar were the names of deities and hewn tree-men. Forest is the hope of the disciples; more learned than the fig is wildest ground.

The *Cedrela odorata* of Brazil is the cedar of Lebanon; of jasper, onyx, and garnet are the hues of the Papilio, which Linnaeus has called the Trojan. There is the Morpho Menelaus whose wings are the garments of Asia. The cigana who pecks the arborescent Arum near lagoons is no bird of *Proverbs*. We know the parables of the wheat and the tares, but the genipapa, the goyava, the mandioca remain unsung.

The holm oak, pond apple, and sumac are Indian. Pale Face is a waif among the Sierras and the mesa, a trespasser upon the savannahs. Bog-moss swaddled the Indian infant; the Mechasipi is savage Virgin Mary; the great lakes are the five tribes of the Iroquois. The red men of America were not amorists; they had no vehement passion for women. Man is sun, water, earth, air, or depraved; head, arms, feet are ground, sea water, woods, or emptied of them, loveless. Unrelated to the desert, the rivers, the forests, man is feeble and a random fornicator.

Amidst a plethora of oak, maple, streams, hummocks, Pale Face is famished for a tree, a little hill, a foal, a clump of sod; utterly sterile, he begs for the Nature he has warped and killed. He cannot be a thinker, a moral animal, until he returns, as a lover, bringing the peace calumet and the grains of tobacco, as a votive offering, to the cliffs and the wilderness which he threw away.

Every country contains the minerals of Paradise or is the barren ground for rough annals. Art without austere weather emasculates the American. The roots of bed-straw washed in a kettle, with the juice of the moose-berry, and pistils of the larch, provide dyes for the Stone Indians. The bark of the aspen and birch is the food of the beaver; these are Laconian arts and meals.

The bison, red deer and antelope crop the meadows near the sources of the Missouri and Assineboine Rivers, which are the pastures for congealed American philosophy. Snow and ice are the grazing grounds of North American metaphysics. Want is the god of the North, desolation is his child; the otter, beaver, and the musquash were the Buddhas of Thoreau. The hardships of explorers were vast moral experiences; Franklin and Parry opened northern straits, Canaan was fathoming the limestone strata of the Sasketchawan fringed with purple dogwood and dwarf birch, and populated by the pelican and the brown fishing eagle. The marmot carried the seeds of the American vetch in its pouch; the head of the geographer contains the Nelson River, Swampy Lake and New Waters.

Lichen and moss sang in your heart; the forest was your brother, poverty the chaste girdle of your bride. Be hardy, and ashamed; modest birds cover themselves with chaff after pleasure; the goose bathes, and others shake their feathers.

Ariel lies to the south; when the pampas is a cocoa orchard and the vintage of Israel—Brazil, Peru, Uruguay, Chile, will be the timbrels, the sackbut, and the harper of the Americas. Quito, Lima, and Cuzco are handlooms; the Mexican valley shall be the home of Apis; emerald and turquoise are the stones of Rahab.

Why does the gillyflower, resembling the spindle which has the scent of Abel's blood, allure us? Give me marl, or rotten leaves which delight the oxen; so that I can be frugal; or hellebore, or danewort, fenugreek to quell all riot, and drive Apis into exile. The slightest wind blows us over, and everything impregnates men. Anaxagoras says that the air contains all seeds, and each time men take a breath they are fornicators; for rain, sleet and flesh are the planters.

Man is water and parched land; fire and rock are his hopes; desire is the Trade Wind; the fruit of the Tucuma palm is the Arcadia of the macaws, and the ruse of mortals. Pumice stone in the Amazons carry the seed of plants, and spawn of freshwater fish as they come down from the remote volcanoes, *Cotopaxi* and *Llanganete* of the Andes; four hundred miles from the Atlantic the throb of Poseidon is felt in the *Tapajos* river. For many weeks' journey one cannot find a pebble in the regions watered by the *Solimoens*. The lower Amazon is hilly; on the shores of the *Teefe* are groves of wild guave and myrtles.

Where are the little hills which shall bring justice, or the fruits of Lebanon? O forest spectre, ferns, lichens, boleti contain Eden. Be primordial or decay.